Conquer Spelling

Grades 4–6

Word Lists, Rules, and Activities

To Help Kids Become Spelling Heroes

Written by Linda Schwartz

Illustrated by Bev Armstrong

The Learning Works

Illustrations: Bev Armstrong
Editor: Kelly Scott
Text Design: Eric Larson, Studio E Books
Cover Illustration: Rick Grayson
Art Director: Tom Cochrane
Cover Designer: Barbara Peterson
Project Director: Linda Schwartz

~ Contents ~

To the Teacher 5
How To Improve Your Spelling 6

Words with Prefixes, Suffixes, and More

How to Divide Words Into Syllables for Easier Spelling 8
Helpful Rules for Better Spelling 9–12
Spelling with Prefixes 13
Words with the Prefixes *co*, *col-*, *con-*, *com-*, and *cor-* 14–15
Words with the Prefix *dis-* 16–17
Words with the Prefix *mis-* 18–20
Words with the Prefix *pre-* 21–22
Words with the Prefix *pro-* 23–25
Words with the Prefix *re-* 26–28
Words with the Prefix *un-* 29–30
Spelling with Suffixes 31
Words with the Suffixes *-able* and *-ible* 32–33
Words with the Suffixes *-ance* and *-ence* 34–35
Words with the Suffixes *-ar, -er, -or,* and *-r* 36–37
Words with the Suffix *-ful* 38–39
Words with the Suffix *-ly* 40–41
Words with the Suffix *-ment* 42–43
Words with the Suffix *-sion* 44–45
Words with the Suffixes *-tion* and *-ion* 46–47
Prefix and Suffix Review 48
Words with *i-e* and *e-i* Spellings 49
Words with *i-c* and *e-i* Spellings #1 50–51
Words with *i-e* and *e-i* Spellings #2 52
Words with *i-e* and *e-i* Review 53
Spelling Words with the Sounds of *-cede, -ceed,* and *-sede* 54
Rules for Spelling Plurals of Nouns 55–56
Spelling Plurals of Nouns 57–58

High-Frequency Word Lists

Spelling Homophones: Word List #1 60–61
Spelling Homophones: Word List #2 62–63
Frequently Misspelled Words #1 64
Frequently Misspelled Words #2 65
Frequently Misspelled Words #3 66
Frequently Misspelled Words #4 67

Words That Are Often Confused 68–69
More Words That Are Often Confused 70–71
Spelling Review 72

Content Area Spelling Words

Science & Math

Bird Words 74
General Science Words #1 75
General Science Words #2 76
Machine Words 77
Mammal Words 78
Plant Words 79
Rain Forest Words 80
Skeleton Words 81–82
Space Words 83
Weather Words 84
Super Challenge Bonus Words #1: Aches and Pains 85
Super Challenge Bonus Words #2: Phobias 86
Super Challenge Bonus Words #3: Fields of Study 87
Super Challenge Bonus Words #4: Math Words 88

Social Studies

Communication Words 89
Early American Colonial Words 90
Family Words 91
General Social Studies Words 92
Geography Words 93
Occupation Words 94
Sports Words 95
Transportation Words 96

Fun with Spelling Words

Activites and Games 98–106
Spelling Progress Charts 107–108

Answer Key 109–112

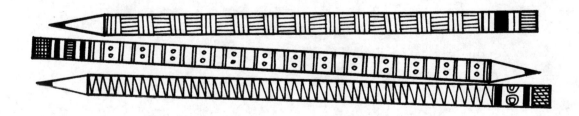

To the Teacher

Conquer Spelling is a practical, easy-to-use book. It is divided into four main sections.

The first section introduces students to words that contain prefixes or suffixes. Basic spelling rules are provided to help students become better spellers. This section also gives tips on how to avoid confusion when spelling words with *i-e* or *e-i*, words with the sounds of *-cede, -ceed*, and *-sede*, and spelling plurals of nouns. Quizzes are provided for each list along with bubble answer keys, so students get practice for standardized tests.

To challenge the gifted and talented students within a self-contained classroom, three bonus words are provided for each spelling list. Teachers can also use these bonus words for extra credit on weekly spelling tests.

The second section contains high-frequency word lists and includes lists of words such as homophones, words that are frequently misspelled, and words that kids often confuse such as stationary–stationery and compliment–complement. Follow-up practice activities are also provided for each of these lists.

The third section of *Conquer Spelling* contains lists of words that are correlated to science and social studies. From mammals to weather—from geography to transportation—these handy word lists are just what a busy teacher needs to correlate to other areas of the curriculum!

The last section is filled with creative, fun activities to use with any of the spelling lists presented in the book. You'll find ideas for using the spelling words to write poems, create word search puzzles, solve codes, and lots more.

A student progress chart is included as well as an answer key for all the follow-up activities. Although rules for spelling are found for specific spelling lists, you'll find all the rules listed together on pages 9–12. Copy these rules for your students and have them keep them in their notebooks for easy reference throughout the school year. A full-color, ready-to-use poster is also included, listing frequently misspelled words—ideal for your language center or bulletin board.

How To Improve Your Spelling

- Use your dictionary to look up unfamiliar words.

- Learn the basic rules of spelling found on pages 9–12.

- Sound words out, and spell them by dividing them into syllables. Rules for dividing words into syllables are found on page 8.

- If you misspell any words on your weekly pretest, study them. Look for ways to help you remember the correct spelling. You can do this in several ways:

  - Say the word to yourself, and look at the shape of each letter.

  - For some words, it may be possible to draw a picture of the part of the word that gives you trouble. This will help you remember the correct spelling.

  - Underline any letters in the word that are stumbling blocks for you.

  - Write the word several times, picturing it in your mind as you write it so you visualize the correct spelling.

  - Make a set of flash cards for the words that give you trouble. Use these cards to help you review for spelling tests.

- On spelling tests and in your everyday writing, take time to proofread what you have written. Look for spelling mistakes. Even spell check programs on computers don't catch everything, especially misuse of homophones such as *their* and *there* or reversals such as *form* and *from*.

- Keep a list of words you often misspell. Study this list until you've mastered the spelling of each word.

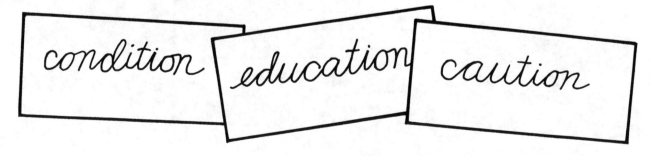

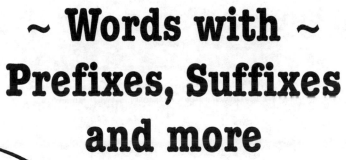

~ Words with ~ Prefixes, Suffixes and more

How to Divide Words Into Syllables for Easier Spelling

Here is a list of rules to help you divide words into syllables.

1. A *syllable* is a group of letters sounded together.

2. Each syllable must have at least one vowel sound; a word cannot have more syllables than vowel sounds.

3. Words pronounced as one syllable should not be divided.

   dive   helped   through

4. A word containing two consonants between two vowels (**vccv**) is divided between the two consonants.

vc-cv	**vc-cv**	**vc-cv**
cor-rect	pret-ty	sis-ter

5. In a two-syllable word containing a single consonant between two vowels (**vcv**), the consonant usually begins the second syllable.

v-cv	**v-cv**
po-tion	to-day

6. In a word ending in *-le*, the consonant immediately preceding the *-le* usually begins the last syllable.

   can-<u>d</u>le   mar-<u>b</u>le   ta-<u>b</u>le

7. Compound words are usually divided between their word parts.

   down-stairs   rain-bow   sun-shine

Helpful Rules for Better Spelling

Rule #1

A *prefix* is a letter or a group of letters added to the beginning of a word to change its meaning.

When the following prefixes are added to a word, the spelling of the word itself stays the same: *dis-, il-, im-, in-, mis-, over-, re-,* and *un-*

examples: disappear, illogical, invest, overboard, unhappy

Rule #2

A *suffix* is a letter or a group of letters added to the end of a word to change its meaning.

When a suffix is added to a word, the spelling of the word generally stays the same, although a final silent *e* is usually dropped if the suffix begins with a vowel.

examples: believable, freedom, powerful, diversity, humorous, hardship, westward

Rule #3

When trying to decide how to spell a word that ends in *-ible* or *-able*, keep these tips in mind:

- Add *-ible* if the root is not a complete word.

    examples: poss<u>i</u>ble, permiss<u>i</u>ble, aud<u>i</u>ble

- Add *-able* if the root forms a complete word.

    examples: suit<u>a</u>ble, depend<u>a</u>ble, comfort<u>a</u>ble

- If a root is a complete word that ends in *e*, drop the *e* and add the suffix *-able.*

    example: valuable (*value + able = valuable*)

Some exceptions to Rule #3: flex<u>ible</u>, respons<u>ible</u>

Helpful Rules for Better Spelling (continued)

Rule #4

When trying to decide whether to use *ie* or *ei*, write *ie* when a word has the sound of long *e*, except after the letter *c*.

> examples: *niece* (has the sound of long *e*.)
> *receive* (has the sound of long *e* but the *ie* follows the letter *c*.)

There are usually exceptions to every rule. Here are a few words that do not follow Rule #4: *neither, weird,* and *seize.* (They are spelled *ei* even though they both have a long *e* sound.)

Rule #5

When the sound of the word is <u>not</u> long *e*, write *ei*, especially when the sound is long *a*.

> examples: *weigh* and *freight*
> examples of exceptions to Rule #5: *mischief, friend*

Rule #6

When trying to decide how to spell a word that has the sound of *-cede*, *-ceed*, or *-sede*, keep these tips in mind:

- Most words with this sound end in *-cede*.
  examples: *recede, concede, precede, secede,* and *accede*

- Only three words end in *-ceed*: *succeed, exceed,* and *proceed.*

- Only one word ends with *-sede*: *supersede*

Rule #7

The most common way to form the plural of a noun is to add an *s*.

> examples: pencil   pencils
> nail   nails

Helpful Rules for Better Spelling (continued)

Rule #8

To form the plural of a noun that ends in the letters *ch, s, sh, z,* or *x,* add *es.*

examples: lun<u>ch</u>   lunches
pa<u>ss</u>   passes
bu<u>sh</u>   bushes
buz<u>z</u>   buzzes
fo<u>x</u>   foxes

Rule #9

To form the plural of a noun that ends in *y* following a consonant, change the *y* to *i* and add *es.*

examples: ba<u>by</u>   babies
ci<u>ty</u>   cities

Rule #10

Instead of adding an *s,* some nouns ending in *f* or *fe* form their plurals by changing the *f* or *fe* to *ve* and adding *s.*

examples: knife   knives
life   lives
leaf   leaves
wife   wives

Rule #11

If a word ends in *o* following a <u>vowel</u>, form the plural by adding *s.*
If a word ends in *o* following a <u>consonant</u>, form the plural by adding *es.*

examples of *o* following a vowel: rad<u>io</u>   radios
cam<u>eo</u>   cameos

example of *o* following a consonant: pota<u>to</u>   potatoes

some exceptions to Rule #11:   so<u>lo</u>   solos
si<u>lo</u>   silos
pia<u>no</u>   pianos

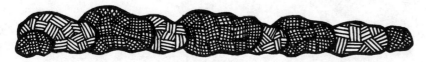

11

Helpful Rules for Better Spelling (continued)

Rule #12

The plurals of some nouns don't follow the regular rules and have unique spellings.

examples:

ox	oxen
tooth	teeth
goose	geese
foot	feet
child	children
woman	women
man	men
mouse	mice

Rule #13

Some nouns are spelled the same in both their singular and plural forms.

examples: deer
sheep
corps
salmon
fowl

Rule #14

In compound words, the plural is formed by making the most important word plural.

examples: sister-in-law   sisters-in-law
(The word *sister* is more important than the words *in* or *law*.)

runner-up   runners-up
(The word *runner* is more important than the word *up*.)

Spelling with Prefixes

Rule #1

A *prefix* is a letter or a group of letters added to the beginning of a word to change its meaning.

When the following prefixes are added to a word, the spelling of the word itself stays the same.

PREFIX	EXAMPLE
mis-	*mis + use = misuse*
dis-	*dis + appear = disappear*
il-	*il + logical = illogical*
im-	*im + mobile = immobile*
in-	*in + visible = invisible*
over-	*over + board = overboard*
re-	*re + unite = reunite*
un-	*un + happy = unhappy*

Words with the Prefixes
co-, col-, con-, com-, and cor-

The prefixes *co-*, *col-*, *con-*, *com-*, and *cor-* add the meaning of "with" to a root word.

~ Word List ~

contract

compare

correct

confide

continue

complain

command

comfort

compound

connect

concern

collection

companion

complete

conductor

* Bonus Words *

congregate

cooperate

coliseum

Words with the Prefixes co-, col-, con-, com-, and cor-

In each group of words, find the one word that is spelled correctly,
and fill in the bubble in front of that word. Then write that spelling word on the line.

1. ○ a. conductar
   ○ b. conducter
   ○ c. conductor
   ○ d. comduckter

   _____

2. ○ a. collection
   ○ b. colection
   ○ c. collectshun
   ○ d. kollection

   _____

3. ○ a. conplete
   ○ b. komplete
   ○ c. complete
   ○ d. complette

   _____

4. ○ a. conect
   ○ b. conneck
   ○ c. konect
   ○ d. connect

   _____

5. ○ a. contrack
   ○ b. contract
   ○ c. kontrack
   ○ d. contrect

   _____

6. ○ a. command
   ○ b. comand
   ○ c. conmand
   ○ d. kommand

   _____

7. ○ a. conplane
   ○ b. complane
   ○ c. complain
   ○ d. complian

   _____

8. ○ a. corract
   ○ b. korrect
   ○ c. corect
   ○ d. correct

   _____

9. ○ a. conpound
   ○ b. compound
   ○ c. compond
   ○ d. compounde

   _____

10. ○ a. contenue
    ○ b. continyou
    ○ c. continue
    ○ d. continnue

   _____

Words with the Prefix dis-

The prefix *dis-* means "not" or "opposite of."

~ **Word List** ~

disable

disclaim

discount

disclose

discover

disband

disarm

discard

discharge

disbelief

disappear

disapprove

disappoint

disagree

disinfect

* **Bonus Words** *

dissatisfy

dissimilar

disintegrate

Words with the Prefix dis- (continued)

In each group of words, find the one word that is spelled correctly,
and fill in the bubble in front of that word. Then write that spelling word on the line.

1. ○ a. disapoint
   ○ b. disappoint
   ○ c. disuppoint
   ○ d. disappiont

   _____

2. ○ a. discuver
   ○ b. discovur
   ○ c. diskover
   ○ d. discover

   _____

3. ○ a. disklaim
   ○ b. disclaim
   ○ c. disklame
   ○ d. disclame

   _____

4. ○ a. disappear
   ○ b. disapear
   ○ c. disappere
   ○ d. dissappear

   _____

5. ○ a. disbeleif
   ○ b. dissbelief
   ○ c. disbelief
   ○ d. disbeelief

   _____

6. ○ a. disenfect
   ○ b. disenfict
   ○ c. disenfectt
   ○ d. disinfect

   _____

7. ○ a. dissapprove
   ○ b. disaprove
   ○ c. disapprove
   ○ d. disappruve

   _____

8. ○ a. disagre
   ○ b. disaggree
   ○ c. dissagree
   ○ d. disagree

   _____

9. ○ a. discuont
   ○ b. discount
   ○ c. diskount
   ○ d. discounte

   _____

10. ○ a. disclothes
    ○ b. discloze
    ○ c. disklose
    ○ d. disclose

    _____

Words with the Prefix mis-

The prefix *mis-* means "bad," "badly," "wrong," or "wrongly."

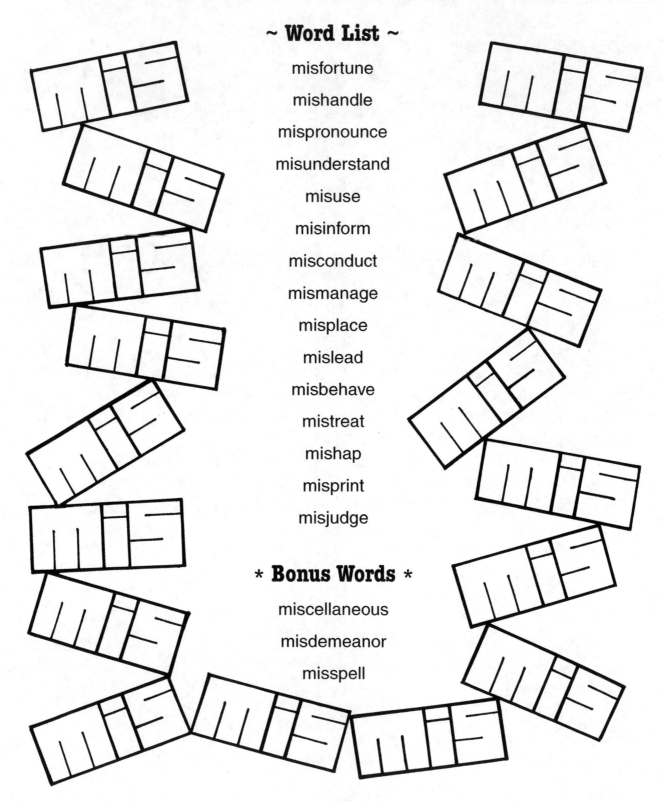

~ Word List ~

misfortune

mishandle

mispronounce

misunderstand

misuse

misinform

misconduct

mismanage

misplace

mislead

misbehave

mistreat

mishap

misprint

misjudge

* Bonus Words *

miscellaneous

misdemeanor

misspell

Words with the Prefix mis- (continued)

In each group of words, find the one word that is spelled correctly,
and fill in the bubble in front of that word. Then write that spelling word on the line.

1. ○ a. misjudge
   ○ b. misjude
   ○ c. misjuge
   ○ d. misjugde

   _____

2. ○ a. misbeehave
   ○ b. misbehave
   ○ c. misbeheve
   ○ d. misbehafe

   _____

3. ○ a. miscunduct
   ○ b. miscondect
   ○ c. miskonduct
   ○ d. misconduct

   _____

4. ○ a. mismanege
   ○ b. mismanage
   ○ c. mismenage
   ○ d. mismanige

   _____

5. ○ a. mishandel
   ○ b. mishandl
   ○ c. mishandle
   ○ d. mishendle

   _____

6. ○ a. mistreet
   ○ b. mistret
   ○ c. mistreat
   ○ d. mistraet

   _____

7. ○ a. misfoutune
   ○ b. misfortune
   ○ c. misfurtune
   ○ d. misfortone

   _____

8. ○ a. mishap
   ○ b. misshap
   ○ c. mishep
   ○ d. mishapp

   _____

9. ○ a. misprenounce
   ○ b. mispronance
   ○ c. mispronounce
   ○ d. misspronounce

   _____

10. ○ a. misleed
    ○ b. misslead
    ○ c. mislede
    ○ d. mislead

   _____

Words with the Prefix mis- (continued)

✱ Match a Meaning

Match each definition to a spelling word by writing the correct letter in front of the word.

_____	1. mispronounce	A. to lead in the wrong direction
_____	2. mismanage	B. to treat badly
_____	3. mistreat	C. to use incorrectly
_____	4. misunderstand	D. to handle incorrectly
_____	5. misplace	E. to be mistaken in judgment
_____	6. misuse	F. to interpret incorrectly
_____	7. misfortune	G. to put in a wrong place
_____	8. mislead	H. an unfortunate incident or event
_____	9. misjudge	I. to pronounce incorrectly

✱ Syllable Count

Use the back of this paper and write:

- seven spelling words from your list that have two syllables

- seven spelling words from your list that have three syllables

- one spelling word from your list that has four syllables

Words with the Prefix pre-

The prefix *pre-* means "prior to," "before," or "in front of."

~ Word List ~

prefer

preview

preform

pregame

prepare

prepay

precise

preschool

present

preserve

presume

preteen

prevail

pretend

prejudge

* Bonus Words *

prescription

preformulate

predicament

Words with the Prefix pre- (continued)

In each group of words, find the one word that is spelled correctly,
and fill in the bubble in front of that word. Then write that spelling word on the line.

1. ○ a. preskool
   ○ b. preschule
   ○ c. preschole
   ○ d. preschool

   _____

2. ○ a. prescent
   ○ b. present
   ○ c. presunt
   ○ d. presant

   _____

3. ○ a. preserve
   ○ b. presurve
   ○ c. precerve
   ○ d. preserrve

   _____

4. ○ a. prejuge
   ○ b. prejodge
   ○ c. prejudge
   ○ d. pregudge

   _____

5. ○ a. prevale
   ○ b. prevail
   ○ c. previal
   ○ d. prevalle

   _____

6. ○ a. prefir
   ○ b. prefur
   ○ c. preffer
   ○ d. prefer

   _____

7. ○ a. presise
   ○ b. precise
   ○ c. precize
   ○ d. presice

   _____

8. ○ a. prepair
   ○ b. prepear
   ○ c. preppare
   ○ d. prepare

   _____

9. ○ a. prezume
   ○ b. pressume
   ○ c. presume
   ○ d. presome

   _____

10. ○ a. preform
    ○ b. preforme
    ○ c. prefform
    ○ d. prefourm

   _____

Words with the Prefix pro-

The prefix *pro-* means "before," "forward," "taking the place of," or "favoring."

~ Word List ~

protect

protest

project

promote

pronoun

provide

produce

program

profile

progress

proclaim

prohibit

protrude

procedure

projector

PROFESSIONAL PROPHETS PROMISE TO PROVIDE PRODIGIOUS PROCLAMATIONS, BUT PROBABLY PREVENT PRODUCTIVITY!

PROTECT PROTESTORS WHO PROMOTE THE PROHIBITION OF PROGRESSIVE PROGRAMS.

* Bonus Words *

procession

proficient

pronunciation

Words with the Prefix pro- (continued)

In each group of words, find the one word that is spelled correctly,
and fill in the bubble in front of that word. Then write that spelling word on the line.

1. ◯ a. proklaim
   ◯ b. procliam
   ◯ c. proclaime
   ◯ d. proclaim

   _____

2. ◯ a. protrood
   ◯ b. protrude
   ◯ c. protrud
   ◯ d. protuede

   _____

3. ◯ a. promoat
   ◯ b. promoate
   ◯ c. promote
   ◯ d. prommote

   _____

4. ◯ a. protect
   ◯ b. prottect
   ◯ c. proteck
   ◯ d. protact

   _____

5. ◯ a. prosedure
   ◯ b. proceedure
   ◯ c. proseedure
   ◯ d. procedure

   _____

6. ◯ a. prohebet
   ◯ b. prohibet
   ◯ c. prohibit
   ◯ d. prohebit

   _____

7. ◯ a. prottest
   ◯ b. protast
   ◯ c. protist
   ◯ d. protest

   _____

8. ◯ a. projekter
   ◯ b. projectur
   ◯ c. projector
   ◯ d. projectir

   _____

9. ◯ a. progrum
   ◯ b. progrem
   ◯ c. programe
   ◯ d. program

   _____

10. ◯ a. profill
    ◯ b. profile
    ◯ c. proffile
    ◯ d. profil

    _____

Words with the Prefix pro- (continued)

✷ Word Search Puzzle

Find and circle each of your spelling words in the puzzle below. The words can be found going up, down, forwards, backwards, and diagonally.

```
A P E N U O N O R P O C
R P R O H I B I T R P L
O Y R J P M A R G O R P
C P R O T R U D E V P A
S K T L C N O A K I R M
S E C G M E P T Y D O P
E K E L Y L D X E E M R
R U T N P O Z U Q S O O
G R O T C E J O R P T D
O A R P R O F I L E E U
R C P R O J E C T K A C
P P N M I A L C O R P E
```

Words with the Prefix re-

The prefix *re-* means "again," "anew," "back," or "backward."

~ Word List ~

reconnect

reject

remain

removable

recovered

recycle

reunite

rebuild

reprint

retrace

received

redirect

rejoice

reminder

reporter

* Bonus Words *

reference

remainder

remembered

Name: _____

Words with the Prefix re- (continued)

In each group of words, find the one word that is spelled correctly,
and fill in the bubble in front of that word. Then write that spelling word on the line.

1. ○ a. recycel
   ○ b. recykle
   ○ c. recycle
   ○ d. resycle

   _____

2. ○ a. removable
   ○ b. removuble
   ○ c. removubel
   ○ d. removeable

   _____

3. ○ a. remindor
   ○ b. remineder
   ○ c. remindur
   ○ d. reminder

   _____

4. ○ a. recieved
   ○ b. received
   ○ c. receeved
   ○ d. reseived

   _____

5. ○ a. retrase
   ○ b. retraise
   ○ c. retrace
   ○ d. retrece

   _____

6. ○ a. rederect
   ○ b. redurect
   ○ c. redirect
   ○ d. rederict

   _____

7. ○ a. repoorter
   ○ b. reporter
   ○ c. reperter
   ○ d. reportor

   _____

8. ○ a. remane
   ○ b. remaine
   ○ c. remain
   ○ d. remian

   _____

9. ○ a. reunite
   ○ b. reunit
   ○ c. reyounite
   ○ d. reunight

   _____

10. ○ a. rejoyce
    ○ b. rejoyse
    ○ c. rejoice
    ○ d. regoice

   _____

Name: _____

Words with the Prefix re- (continued)

✳ Missing Vowels

Fill in the missing vowels to spell words on your spelling list.

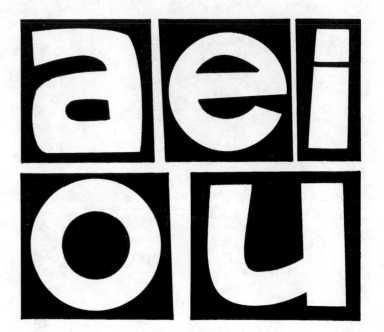

1. r __ m __ __ n

2. r __ t r __ c __

3. r __ m __ n d __ r

4. r __ d __ r __ c t

5. r __ m __ v __ b l __

6. r __ b __ __ l d

7. r __ p __ r t __ r

8. r __ c __ v __ r __ d

✳ Match a Meaning

Match each definition to a spelling word by writing the correct letter in front of the word.

_____ 1. rejoice   A. got back or regained

_____ 2. rebuild   B. to refuse to accept

_____ 3. reporter   C. to show or feel great joy

_____ 4. reunite   D. to stay

_____ 5. retrace   E. to use again

_____ 6. reject   F. to build again

_____ 7. redirect   G. to trace again or go back over

_____ 8. remain   H. to bring together again

_____ 9. recovered   I. to change the course or direction of

_____ 10. recycle   J. one who reports the news

Name: _____

Words with the Prefix re- (continued)

✳ Missing Vowels

Fill in the missing vowels to spell words on your spelling list.

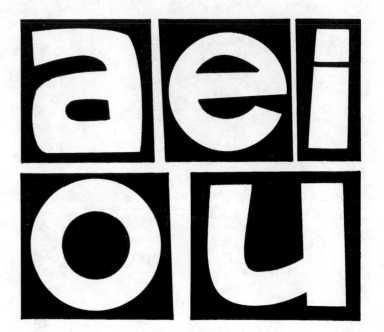

1. r __ m __ __ n
2. r __ t r __ c __
3. r __ m __ n d __ r
4. r __ d __ r __ c t
5. r __ m __ v __ b l __
6. r __ b __ __ l d
7. r __ p __ r t __ r
8. r __ c __ v __ r __ d

✳ Match a Meaning

Match each definition to a spelling word by writing the correct letter in front of the word.

_____ 1. rejoice   A. got back or regained

_____ 2. rebuild   B. to refuse to accept

_____ 3. reporter   C. to show or feel great joy

_____ 4. reunite   D. to stay

_____ 5. retrace   E. to use again

_____ 6. reject   F. to build again

_____ 7. redirect   G. to trace again or go back over

_____ 8. remain   H. to bring together again

_____ 9. recovered   I. to change the course or direction of

_____ 10. recycle   J. one who reports the news

Conquer Spelling
Copyright © 2003 The Learning Works

28

Words with the Prefix un-

The prefix *un-* means "not," "do the opposite of," or "deprive of."

~ Word List ~

unbutton

unable

unreal

unlock

unbeaten

uncover

unwilling

unattached

unarmed

unlucky

undivided

unfinished

unfriendly

uncooked

undefeated

* Bonus Words *

unimportant

unquestionable

uncomfortable

Words with the Prefix un- (continued)

In each group of words, find the one word that is spelled correctly,
and fill in the bubble in front of that word. Then write that spelling word on the line.

1. ◯ a. unfreindly
    ◯ b. unfriendlly
    ◯ c. unfriendly
    ◯ d. unfreendly

    _____

2. ◯ a. unduvided
    ◯ b. undivided
    ◯ c. unduviddcd
    ◯ d. undevided

    _____

3. ◯ a. unkover
    ◯ b. uncovver
    ◯ c. uncover
    ◯ d. uncovor

    _____

4. ◯ a. unbeeten
    ◯ b. unbeetan
    ◯ c. unbeaton
    ◯ d. unbeaten

    _____

5. ◯ a. unatached
    ◯ b. unattached
    ◯ c. unatteched
    ◯ d. unattahed

    _____

6. ◯ a. undafeated
    ◯ b. undefeeted
    ◯ c. undefeated
    ◯ d. undufeated

    _____

7. ◯ a. unlucky
    ◯ b. unluckee
    ◯ c. unlcuky
    ◯ d. unllucky

    _____

8. ◯ a. unbuttin
    ◯ b. unbuttun
    ◯ c. unbutton
    ◯ d. unbutten

    _____

9. ◯ a. undivideed
    ◯ b. undevided
    ◯ c. unduvided
    ◯ d. undivided

    _____

10. ◯ a. unfinished
    ◯ b. unfenished
    ◯ c. unfineshed
    ◯ d. unfinnished

    _____

Spelling with Suffixes

Rule #2

A *suffix* is a letter or a group of letters added to the end of a word. A suffix can change the meaning of the root word or can form a new word. Here are some common suffixes that can be added to root words:

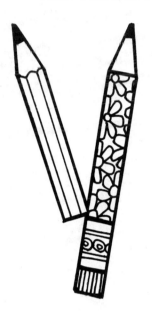

-able	-ist
-age	-ity
-ance	-ive
-ancy	-logy
-ant	-ment
-dom	-ness
-ence	-ory
-er	-ous
-ful	-ship
-hood	-some
-ion	-tude
-ish	-ward
-ism	-y

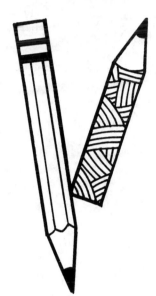

Rule #3

When trying to decide how to spell a word that ends in *-ible* or *-able*, keep these tips in mind:

- Add *-ible* if the root is not a complete word.

  examples: <u>poss</u>ible, <u>permiss</u>ible, <u>aud</u>ible

- Add *-able* if the root forms a complete word.

  examples: <u>suit</u>able, <u>depend</u>able, <u>comfort</u>able

- If a root is a complete word that ends in *e*, drop the *e* and add the suffix *-able*.

  example: valuable (value + *able* = valuable)

Some exceptions to rule #3: flex<u>ible</u>, respons<u>ible</u>, change<u>able</u>

Words with the Suffixes -able and -ible

The suffixes *-able* and *-ible* mean "capable" or "worthy of."

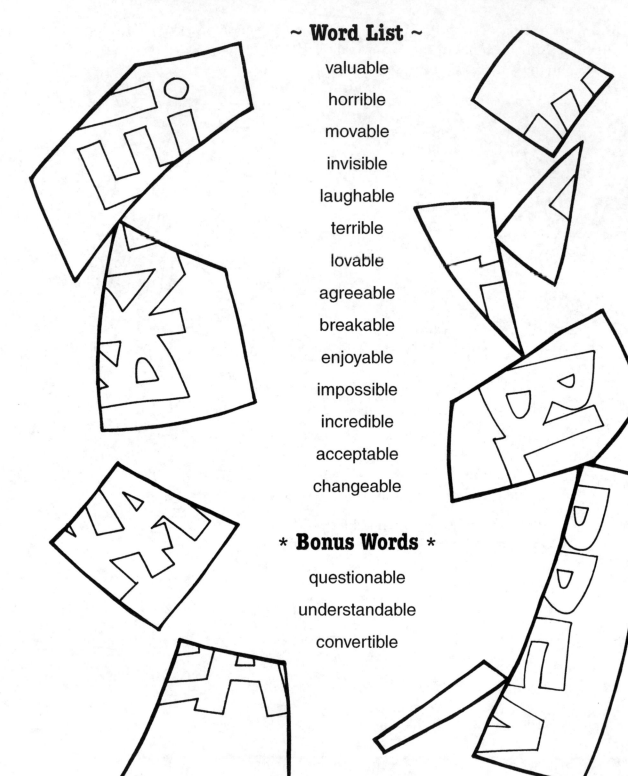

~ Word List ~

valuable

horrible

movable

invisible

laughable

terrible

lovable

agreeable

breakable

enjoyable

impossible

incredible

acceptable

changeable

* Bonus Words *

questionable

understandable

convertible

Words with the Suffixes -able and -ible (continued)

In each group of words, find the one word that is spelled correctly,
and fill in the bubble in front of that word. Then write that spelling word on the line.

1. ○ a. aceptable
   ○ b. accepttible
   ○ c. acceptible
   ○ d. acceptable

   _____

2. ○ a. changeable
   ○ b. changible
   ○ c. changeible
   ○ d. changable

   _____

3. ○ a. inposable
   ○ b. impossable
   ○ c. impossible
   ○ d. inpossible

   _____

4. ○ a. horribel
   ○ b. horrible
   ○ c. horrable
   ○ d. horable

   _____

5. ○ a. envisible
   ○ b. envisable
   ○ c. invesible
   ○ d. invisible

   _____

6. ○ a. breekible
   ○ b. braekable
   ○ c. breakible
   ○ d. breakable

   _____

7. ○ a. encredable
   ○ b. incredible
   ○ c. incredable
   ○ d. encredible

   _____

8. ○ a. aggreable
   ○ b. aggreible
   ○ c. agreebile
   ○ d. agreeable

   _____

9. ○ a. valuable
   ○ b. valluable
   ○ c. valuabile
   ○ d. valueable

   _____

10. ○ a. moveable
    ○ b. movabile
    ○ c. movable
    ○ d. muvable

    _____

Words with the Suffixes -ance and -ence

The suffixes *-ance* and *-ence* mean "an act," "process," or "state of being."

~ Word List ~

endurance

audience

confidence

experience

ambulance

fragrance

reference

attendance

appearance

conference

admittance

defiance

interference

difference

preference

* Bonus Words *

remembrance

independence

coincidence

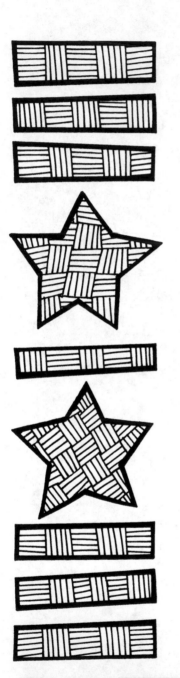
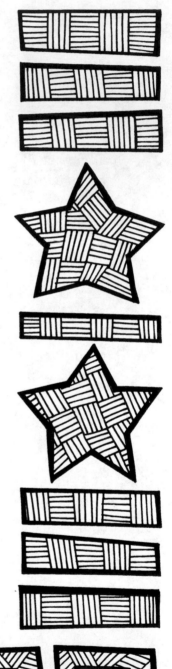

Words with the Suffixes -ance and -ence (continued)

In each group of words, find the one word that is spelled correctly,
and fill in the bubble in front of that word. Then write that spelling word on the line.

1. ○ a. endurance
   ○ b. endurence
   ○ c. indurence
   ○ d. indurance

   _____

2. ○ a. admitance
   ○ b. admittence
   ○ c. addmittance
   ○ d. admittance

   _____

3. ○ a. differance
   ○ b. diference
   ○ c. difference
   ○ d. defference

   _____

4. ○ a. appearence
   ○ b. appearance
   ○ c. apearance
   ○ d. appeerence

   _____

5. ○ a. anbulance
   ○ b. ambulence
   ○ c. ambullance
   ○ d. ambulance

   _____

6. ○ a. reference
   ○ b. refference
   ○ c. referance
   ○ d. refreance

   _____

7. ○ a. konfidence
   ○ b. konfidance
   ○ c. confidence
   ○ d. confidance

   _____

8. ○ a. expereince
   ○ b. experiance
   ○ c. esperience
   ○ d. experience

   _____

9. ○ a. deefiance
   ○ b. definance
   ○ c. defiance
   ○ d. defiaence

   _____

10. ○ a. conferance
    ○ b. conference
    ○ c. konference
    ○ d. konferance

    _____

Words with the Suffixes -ar, -er, -or, and -r

The suffixes *-ar, -er, -or,* and *-r* mean "one who" or "that which."

~ Word List ~

liar

officer

actor

beggar

buyer

collector

container

director

quarter

recorder

sailor

superior

visitor

sweater

protector

* Bonus Words *

bookkeeper

interviewer

supervisor

Words with the Suffixes -ar, -er, -or, and -r (continued)

In each group of words, find the one word that is spelled correctly,
and fill in the bubble in front of that word. Then write that spelling word on the line.

1. ○ a. beggar
   ○ b. begger
   ○ c. begar
   ○ d. beger

   _____

2. ○ a. visiter
   ○ b. visitar
   ○ c. visitor
   ○ d. vesitor

   _____

3. ○ a. swaeter
   ○ b. sweater
   ○ c. sweator
   ○ d. sweatar

   _____

4. ○ a. buier
   ○ b. buyor
   ○ c. buyar
   ○ d. buyer

   _____

5. ○ a. kollector
   ○ b. kollecter
   ○ c. collector
   ○ d. collectar

   _____

6. ○ a. quartar
   ○ b. quartor
   ○ c. quarter
   ○ d. kwarter

   _____

7. ○ a. saleor
   ○ b. saler
   ○ c. sailar
   ○ d. sailor

   _____

8. ○ a. superior
   ○ b. superrior
   ○ c. superier
   ○ d. superiar

   _____

9. ○ a. protecter
   ○ b. protectar
   ○ c. protector
   ○ d. protechtor

   _____

10. ○ a. kontainor
    ○ b. contianor
    ○ c. containor
    ○ d. container

    _____

Name: _____

Words with the Suffix -ful

The suffix *-ful* means "full of" or "number or quality that fills."

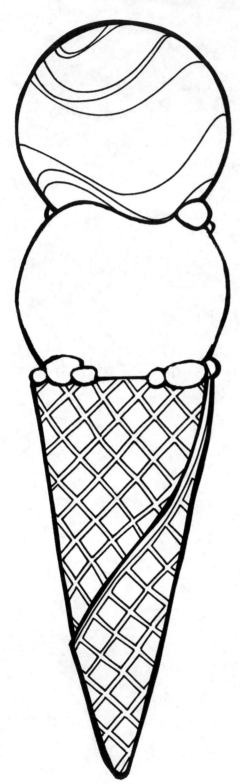

~ Word List ~

awful

roomful

hopeful

successful

harmful

wonderful

thoughtful

uneventful

peaceful

careful

delightful

beautiful

fearful

plentiful

shameful

* Bonus Words *

mournful

bountiful

unhealthful

Words with the Suffix -ful (continued)

In each group of words, find the one word that is spelled correctly,
and fill in the bubble in front of that word. Then write that spelling word on the line.

1. ○ a. hopful
   ○ b. hopefull
   ○ c. hopeful
   ○ d. hoppful

   _____

2. ○ a. sucesful
   ○ b. sucessful
   ○ c. succesful
   ○ d. successful

   _____

3. ○ a. thoughtful
   ○ b. thoutful
   ○ c. thouhgful
   ○ d. thoughtfull

   _____

4. ○ a. pletnyful
   ○ b. plentifull
   ○ c. plentiful
   ○ d. plantiful

   _____

5. ○ a. wondorful
   ○ b. wonderful
   ○ c. onederful
   ○ d. wonderfull

   _____

6. ○ a. deelightful
   ○ b. deliteful
   ○ c. delighttful
   ○ d. delightful

   _____

7. ○ a. shameful
   ○ b. shamful
   ○ c. shammeful
   ○ d. shamefull

   _____

8. ○ a. uneventfull
   ○ b. unevenful
   ○ c. unevantful
   ○ d. uneventful

   _____

9. ○ a. hopful
   ○ b. hopefull
   ○ c. hopeful
   ○ d. hoppful

   _____

10. ○ a. beautifull
    ○ b. beeutiful
    ○ c. beautifful
    ○ d. beautiful

    _____

Words with the Suffix -ly

The suffix *-ly* changes a noun into an adjective, or an adjective into an adverb.

~ Word List ~

bravely

casually

excitedly

suddenly

closely

elderly

quarterly

exactly

carelessly

lonely

completely

fearlessly

incorrectly

breathlessly

thoughtfully

* Bonus Words *

supposedly

accidentally

immediately

Words with the Suffix -ly (continued)

In each group of words, find the one word that is spelled correctly,
and fill in the bubble in front of that word. Then write that spelling word on the line.

1. ○ a. completly
   ○ b. compleatly
   ○ c. completely
   ○ d. kompletely

   _____

2. ○ a. sudenly
   ○ b. suddenly
   ○ c. suddinly
   ○ d. suddenlly

   _____

3. ○ a. klosely
   ○ b. closly
   ○ c. closely
   ○ d. closeily

   _____

4. ○ a. incorrectly
   ○ b. encorectly
   ○ c. encorrectly
   ○ d. incorectly

   _____

5. ○ a. thoughfully
   ○ b. thoughtfuly
   ○ c. thoughtfully
   ○ d. thoughfuly

   _____

6. ○ a. karelesly
   ○ b. carelessly
   ○ c. carelesly
   ○ d. karelessly

   _____

7. ○ a. exactly
   ○ b. ixactly
   ○ c. exactlly
   ○ d. exactely

   _____

8. ○ a. kwarterly
   ○ b. querterly
   ○ c. quarterly
   ○ d. quartorly

   _____

9. ○ a. lonly
   ○ b. lonily
   ○ c. loanly
   ○ d. lonely

   _____

10. ○ a. breathlesly
    ○ b. breathlissly
    ○ c. breathlessly
    ○ d. brethlessly

    _____

Words with the Suffix -ment

The suffix *-ment* means "act," "process of," or "condition."

~Word List~

enjoyment

apartment

placement

statement

argument

pavement

equipment

government

department

improvement

experiment

entertainment

compliment

temperament

fulfillment

* Bonus Words *

entanglement

complement

containment

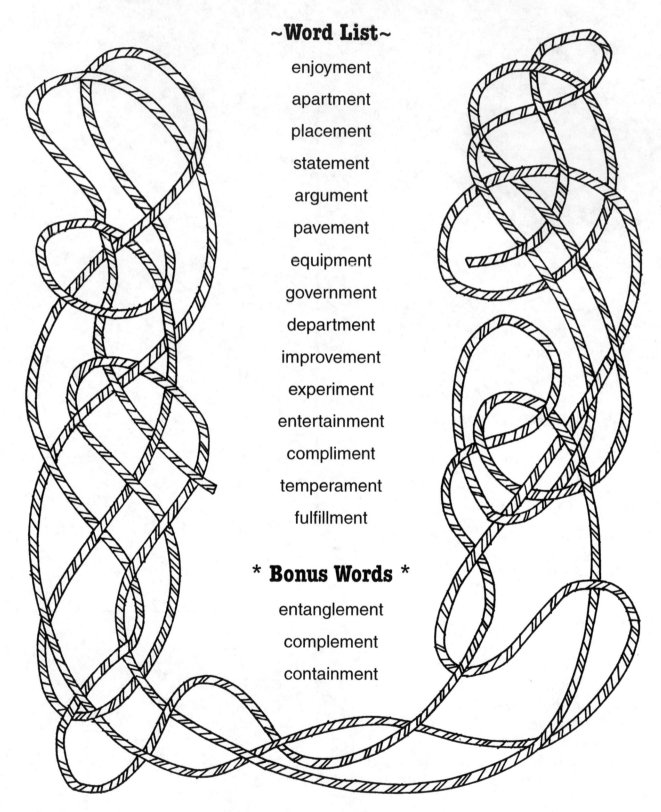

Words with the Suffix -ment (continued)

In each group of words, find the one word that is spelled correctly,
and fill in the bubble in front of that word. Then write that spelling word on the line.

1. ○ a. arguement
   ○ b. argyoument
   ○ c. argument
   ○ d. aregument

   _____

2. ○ a. goverment
   ○ b. guverment
   ○ c. govornment
   ○ d. government

   _____

3. ○ a. equiptment
   ○ b. equepment
   ○ c. equipment
   ○ d. equipmint

   _____

4. ○ a. fullfillment
   ○ b. fulfillment
   ○ c. fulfilment
   ○ d. falfillment

   _____

5. ○ a. placement
   ○ b. placmment
   ○ c. placemint
   ○ d. plasement

   _____

6. ○ a. esperiment
   ○ b. expirament
   ○ c. experament
   ○ d. experiment

   _____

7. ○ a. pavment
   ○ b. pavement
   ○ c. pavemint
   ○ d. payvement

   _____

8. ○ a. appartment
   ○ b. upartment
   ○ c. apartment
   ○ d. aparttment

   _____

9. ○ a. emprovment
   ○ b. improvement
   ○ c. impruvement
   ○ d. inprovement

   _____

10. ○ a. injoyment
    ○ b. enjoiment
    ○ c. enjoyment
    ○ d. enjoyement

   _____

43

Words with the Suffix -sion

The suffix *-sion* changes a verb or an adjective into a noun.

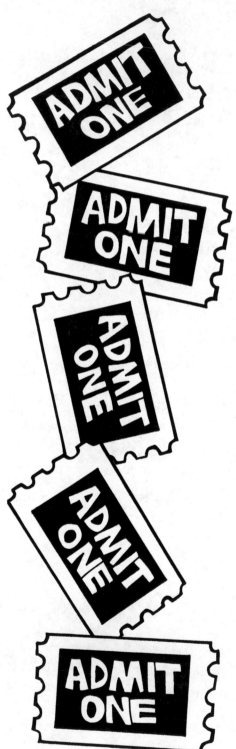

~ Word List ~

tension

confession

extension

explosion

decision

discussion

admission

expansion

division

confusion

permission

television

erosion

collision

invasion

* Bonus Words *

comprehension

possession

recession

Words with the Suffix -sion (continued)

In each group of words, find the one word that is spelled correctly,
and fill in the bubble in front of that word. Then write that spelling word on the line.

1. ○ a. television
   ○ b. telivision
   ○ c. tellevision
   ○ d. tellivision

   _____

2. ○ a. envasion
   ○ b. invassion
   ○ c. envassion
   ○ d. invasion

   _____

3. ○ a. discusion
   ○ b. descussion
   ○ c. deskussion
   ○ d. discussion

   _____

4. ○ a. espansion
   ○ b. expansion
   ○ c. expanssion
   ○ d. expension

   _____

5. ○ a. konfession
   ○ b. cunfession
   ○ c. confession
   ○ d. confesion

   _____

6. ○ a. extension
   ○ b. extinsion
   ○ c. extenssion
   ○ d. ixtension

   _____

7. ○ a. purmission
   ○ b. premission
   ○ c. permision
   ○ d. permission

   _____

8. ○ a. confuzion
   ○ b. konfusion
   ○ c. confusion
   ○ d. confussion

   _____

9. ○ a. addmission
   ○ b. admision
   ○ c. admishun
   ○ d. admission

   _____

10. ○ a. kollision
    ○ b. collision
    ○ c. colision
    ○ d. kolision

    _____

Words with the Suffixes -tion and -ion

The suffixes *-tion* and *-ion* mean "act," "condition," "state," or "process of."

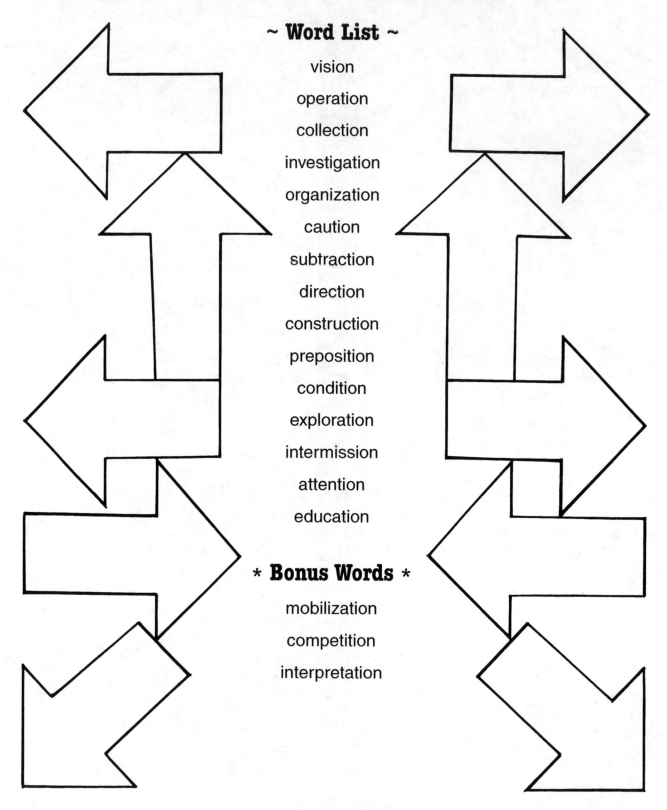

~ **Word List** ~

vision

operation

collection

investigation

organization

caution

subtraction

direction

construction

preposition

condition

exploration

intermission

attention

education

* **Bonus Words** *

mobilization

competition

interpretation

Words with the Suffixes -tion and -ion (continued)

In each group of words, find the one word that is spelled correctly,
and fill in the bubble in front of that word. Then write that spelling word on the line.

1. ○ a. cuation
   ○ b. causion
   ○ c. caution
   ○ d. kaution

   _____

2. ○ a. konstruction
   ○ b. construction
   ○ c. constructsion
   ○ d. consturction

   _____

3. ○ a. investigation
   ○ b. envestigation
   ○ c. invistigation
   ○ d. investigasion

   _____

4. ○ a. oporation
   ○ b. operatetion
   ○ c. operation
   ○ d. operasion

   _____

5. ○ a. perposition
   ○ b. propersition
   ○ c. prepositshun
   ○ d. preposition

   _____

6. ○ a. intermission
   ○ b. entermision
   ○ c. entermission
   ○ d. intermision

   _____

7. ○ a. atention
   ○ b. attenshun
   ○ c. attention
   ○ d. atenttion

   _____

8. ○ a. expurlation
   ○ b. exploration
   ○ c. esploration
   ○ d. expleration

   _____

9. ○ a. orgunization
   ○ b. orginization
   ○ c. organizasion
   ○ d. organization

   _____

10. ○ a. subtracktion
    ○ b. subtrection
    ○ c. subtraction
    ○ d. subtractshun

   _____

Prefix and Suffix Review

In each group of words, find the one word that is spelled *incorrectly*,
and fill in the bubble in front of that word. Then write that spelling word on the line.

1. ○ a. misprint
   ○ b. unatached
   ○ c. thoughtful
   ○ d. placement

   _____

2. ○ a. temperment
   ○ b. admission
   ○ c. undivided
   ○ d. projector

   _____

3. ○ a. officer
   ○ b. plentiful
   ○ c. preferance
   ○ d. misinform

   _____

4. ○ a. companion
   ○ b. unwilling
   ○ c. attendence
   ○ d. defiance

   _____

5. ○ a. endurence
   ○ b. preschool
   ○ c. received
   ○ d. disable

   _____

6. ○ a. director
   ○ b. unfinished
   ○ c. differance
   ○ d. beautiful

   _____

7. ○ a. mispronounce
   ○ b. continue
   ○ c. komplain
   ○ d. disappear

   _____

8. ○ a. prohibit
   ○ b. present
   ○ c. recycle
   ○ d. removeable

   _____

9. ○ a. misbehave
   ○ b. prosedure
   ○ c. reminder
   ○ d. undefeated

   _____

10. ○ a. mismanage
    ○ b. presume
    ○ c. unfriendly
    ○ d. interfearance

    _____

Words with i-e and e-i Spellings

Rule #4

When trying to decide whether to use *ie* or *ei*, write *ie* when a word has the sound of long *e*, except after the letter *c*.

examples: *niece* (has the sound of long *e*.)
receive (has the sound of long *e* but the *ei* follows the letter *c*.)

There are usually exceptions to every rule. Here are a few words that do not follow Rule #4:

neither, leisure, either, and *seize*
(They are spelled *ei* even though they have a long *e* sound.)

Rule #5

When the sound of the word is <u>not</u> long *e*, write *ei*, especially when the sound is long *a*.

examples: *weigh* and *freight*

examples of exceptions to Rule #5: *mischief, friend*

Words with i-e and e-i Spellings #1

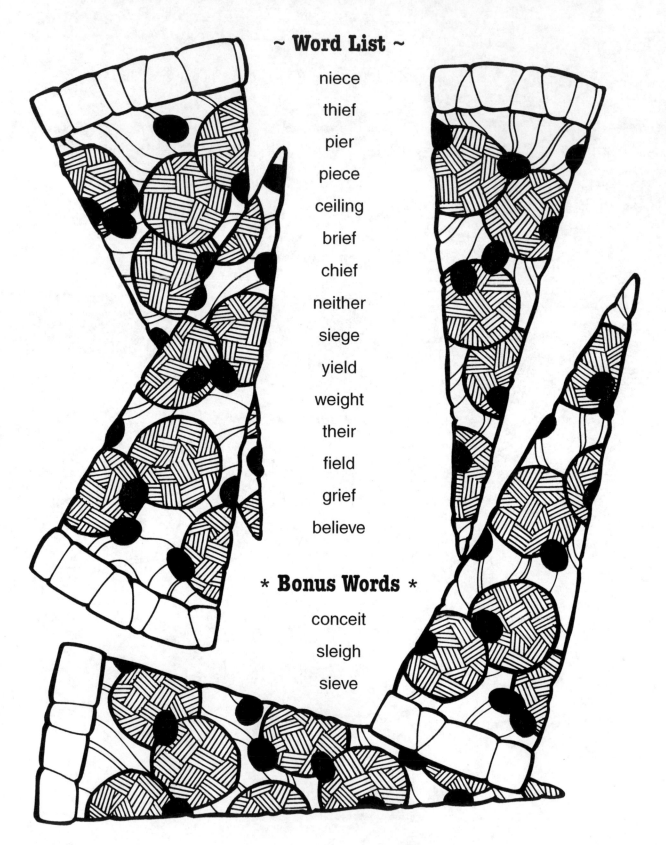

~ Word List ~

niece

thief

pier

piece

ceiling

brief

chief

neither

siege

yield

weight

their

field

grief

believe

* Bonus Words *

conceit

sleigh

sieve

Words with i-e and e-i Spellings #1 (continued)

Fill in the bubble for the word that is spelled correctly in each pair.

1. ○ a. neice
   ○ b. niece

2. ○ a. cheif
   ○ b chief

3. ○ a. ceiling
   ○ b. cieling

4. ○ a. neither
   ○ b. niether

5. ○ a. beleive
   ○ b. believe

6. ○ a. yeild
   ○ b. yield

7. ○ a. greif
   ○ b. grief

8. ○ a. feild
   ○ b. field

9. ○ a. seige
   ○ b. siege

10. ○ a. their
    ○ b. thier

11. ○ a. theif
    ○ b. thief

12. ○ a. peir
    ○ b. pier

13. ○ a. peice
    ○ b. piece

14. ○ a. breif
    ○ b. brief

15. ○ a. weight
    ○ b. wieght

Words with i-e and e-i Spellings #2

~ Word List ~

fierce

efficient

perceive

reign

mischief

friend

achieve

deceive

ancient

leisure

fiery

relieve

preview

receive

freight

* Bonus Words *

counterfeit

weird

handkerchief

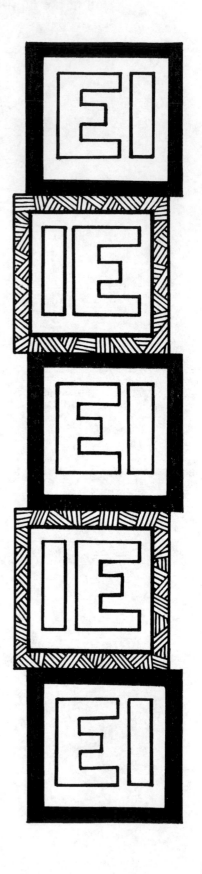

Words with i-e and e-i Review

In each group of words, find the one word that is spelled correctly,
and fill in the bubble in front of that word. Then write that spelling word on the line.

1. ○ a. cheif
   ○ b. yield
   ○ c. vien
   ○ d. frieght

   _____

2. ○ a. releif
   ○ b. neice
   ○ c. greif
   ○ d. receive

   _____

3. ○ a. foreign
   ○ b. liesure
   ○ c. wierd
   ○ d. sieze

   _____

4. ○ a. niether
   ○ b. feiry
   ○ c. perceive
   ○ d. decieve

   _____

5. ○ a. breif
   ○ b. niether
   ○ c. efficient
   ○ d. acheive

   _____

6. ○ a. feirce
   ○ b. ancient
   ○ c. cieling
   ○ d. preveiw

   _____

★ Missing Vowels

Complete the correct spelling of each word by filling in the blanks with *ei* or *ie*.

1. w __ __ ght
2. f __ __ ld
3. f r __ __ nd
4. p __ __ r

5. misch __ __ f
6. r __ __ gn
7. s __ __ ge
8. bel __ __ ve

Spelling Words with the Sounds of -cede, -ceed, and -sede

Rule #6

When trying to decide how to spell a word that has the sound of *-cede*, *-ceed*, or *-sede*, keep these tips in mind.

- Most words with this sound end in *-cede*.

  examples: *recede, concede, precede, secede,* and *accede*

- Only three words end in *-ceed*: *succeed, exceed,* and *proceed.*

- Only one word ends with *-sede*: *supersede*

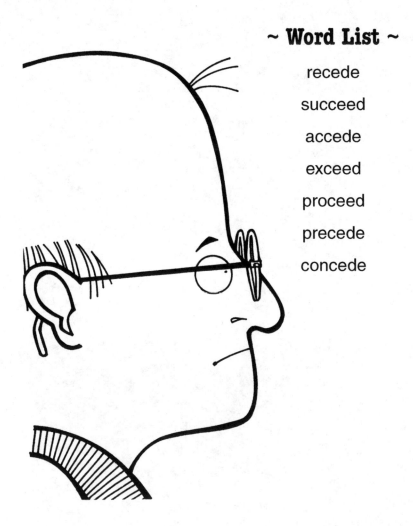

~ Word List ~

recede

succeed

accede

exceed

proceed

precede

concede

Rules for Spelling Plurals of Nouns

Rule #7

The most common way to form the plural of a noun is to add an *s*.

examples: pencil   pencils
          nail   nails

Rule #8

To form the plural of a noun that ends in the letters *ch, s, sh, z,* or *x,* add *es.*

examples: lun<u>ch</u>   lunches
          pa<u>ss</u>   passes
          bu<u>sh</u>   bushes
          bu<u>zz</u>   buzzes
          fo<u>x</u>   foxes

Rule #9

To form the plural of a noun that ends in *y* following a consonant, change the *y* to *i* and add *es.*

examples: ba<u>by</u>   babies
          ci<u>ty</u>   cities
          cher<u>ry</u> cherries

Rule #10

Instead of adding an *s,* some nouns ending in *f* or *fe* form their plurals by changing the *f* or *fe* to *ve* and adding *s.*

examples: knife   knives
          life   lives
          leaf   leaves
          wife   wives
          elf   elves

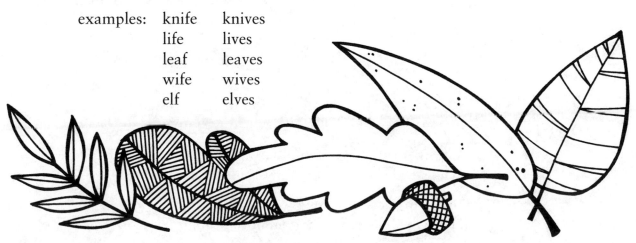

Rules for Spelling Plurals of Nouns (continued)

Rule #11

If a word ends in *o* following a <u>vowel</u>, form the plural by adding *s*.
If a word ends in *o* following a <u>consonant</u>, form the plural by adding *es*.

| examples of *o* following a vowel: | rad<u>i</u>o | radios |
| | cam<u>e</u>o | cameos |

| example of *o* following a consonant: | pota<u>t</u>o | potatoes |

some exceptions to Rule #11:	so<u>l</u>o	solos
	si<u>l</u>o	silos
	pia<u>n</u>o	pianos

Rule #12

The plurals of some nouns don't follow the regular rules and have unique spellings.

examples:	ox	oxen	child	children
	tooth	teeth	woman	women
	goose	geese	man	men
	foot	feet	mouse	mice

Rule #13

Some nouns are spelled the same in both their singular and plural forms.

examples: deer
sheep
corps
salmon
fowl

Rule #14

In compound words, the plural is formed by making the more important word plural.

examples: sister-in-law   sisters-in-law
(The word *sister* is more important than the word *law*.)

runner-up   runners-up
(The word *runner* is more important than the word *up*.)

Spelling Plurals of Nouns

Fill in the bubble for the plural that is spelled correctly in each pair.

1. ○ a. babys
   ○ b. babies

2. ○ a. lunchs
   ○ b. lunches

3. ○ a. knives
   ○ b. knifes

4. ○ a. tomatoes
   ○ b. tomatos

5. ○ a. cherries
   ○ b. cherrys

6. ○ a. pencils
   ○ b. penciles

7. ○ a. oxs
   ○ b. oxen

8. ○ a. women
   ○ b. womans

9. ○ a. mouses
   ○ b. mice

10. ○ a. radios
    ○ b. radioes

11. ○ a. buzzs
    ○ b. buzzes

12. ○ a. cities
    ○ b. citys

13. ○ a. leafs
    ○ b. leaves

14. ○ a. lives
    ○ b. lifes

15. ○ a. teeth
    ○ b. tooths

16. ○ a. sheep
    ○ b. sheeps

17. ○ a. pianos
    ○ b. pianoes

18. ○ a. potatos
    ○ b. potatoes

19. ○ a. feet
    ○ b. foots

20. ○ a. childs
    ○ b. children

Spelling Plurals of Nouns

Fill in the bubble for the plural that is spelled correctly in each pair.

1. ○ a. mans
   ○ b. men

2. ○ a. deer
   ○ b. deers

3. ○ a. brothers-in-law
   ○ b. brother-in-laws

4. ○ a. siloes
   ○ b. silos

5. ○ a. wifes
   ○ b. wives

6. ○ a. bushs
   ○ b. bushes

7. ○ a. cameos
   ○ b. cameoes

8. ○ a. runner-ups
   ○ b. runners-up

9. ○ a. salmons
   ○ b. salmon

10. ○ a. shelfs
    ○ b. shelves

11. ○ a. territorys
    ○ b. territiories

12. ○ a. kangaroos
    ○ b. kangarooes

13. ○ a. ghosts
    ○ b. ghostes

14. ○ a. deputies
    ○ b. deputys

15. ○ a. axs
    ○ b. axes

16. ○ a. sopranoes
    ○ b. sopranos

17. ○ a. countries
    ○ b. countrys

18. ○ a. flys
    ○ b. flies

19. ○ a. authoritys
    ○ b. authorities

20. ○ a. embargos
    ○ b. embargoes

~ High-Frequency ~
Word Lists

Spelling Homophones: Word List #1

Homophones are words that sound alike but have different spellings and meanings.

~ Word List ~

yoke	yolk
plain	plane
waist	waste
great	grate
throne	thrown
hoarse	horse
beach	beech
flour	flower
scene	seen
capital	capitol
aisle	isle
knead	need
straight	strait
allowed	aloud
hangar	hanger

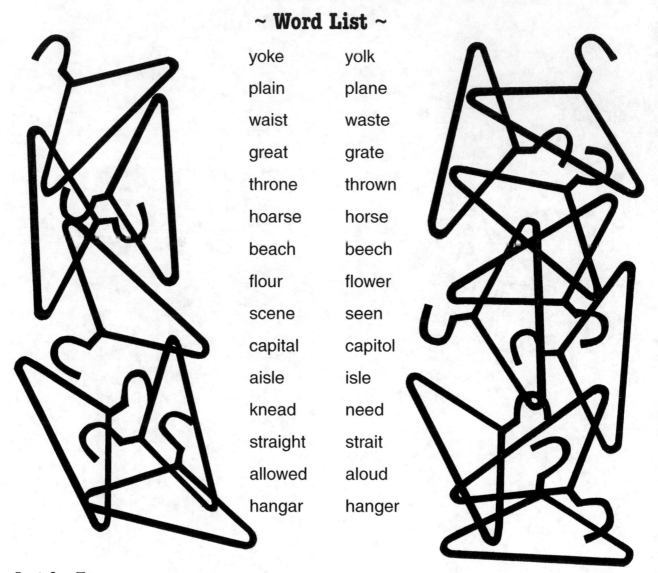

✱ Just for Fun

Pick six pairs of homophones from the list. Draw a picture of each word to show you understand its meaning. Label each word as shown below.

Homophone Review: Word List #1

Write the homophone(s) from word list #1 that correctly complete(s) each sentence.

1. The students were _____ to read their stories _____ to the class.

2. The recipe called for an egg _____ and one cup of _____.

3. The _____ of California is Sacramento.

4. My voice is so _____ I can hardly talk.

5. The cowgirl was _____ from the _____.

6. I _____ to _____ the carrots for the salad I am making.

7. The _____ was in the _____ at the airport while the engine was being repaired.

8. The kids built a sand castle at the _____.

9. This sundae is _____ but it's going to add inches to my _____.

10. The boat sailed through the narrow _____ and out to sea.

11. I hung the shirt on a plastic _____.

12. The lawyers met in the _____ building.

Spelling Homophones: Word List #2

Homophones are words that sound alike but have different spellings and meanings.

~ Word List ~

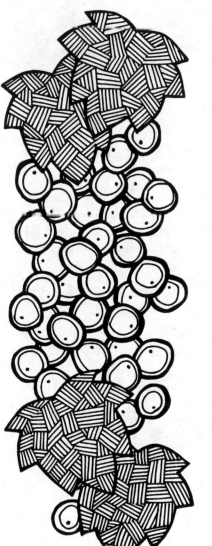
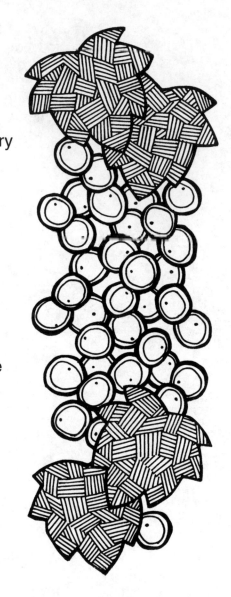

suite	sweet
foul	fowl
counsel	council
stationary	stationery
colonel	kernel
piece	peace
thyme	lime
coarse	course
currant	current
shear	sheer
principal	principle
cymbal	symbol
quarts	quartz
plain	plane
foreword	forward

* Just for Fun

Take the Homophone Challenge and make a list of 200 or more pairs of homophones!

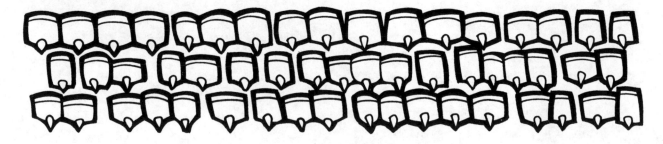

Homophone Review: Word List #2

Circle the correct homophone for each description.

1. fruit used in making jelly   current   currant

2. a musical instrument   cymbal   symbol

3. a barnyard bird   fowl   foul

4. writing paper   stationary   stationery

5. a spice   time   thyme

6. the head of a school   principal   principle

7. to cut   shear   sheer

8. rough   course   coarse

9. an officer   kernel   colonel

10. to advise   counsel   council

✱ Just for Fun

Write a sentence for each of the homophones that is *not* circled in the exercise above. Underline the homophones in your sentences.

Frequently Misspelled Words #1

~ Word List ~

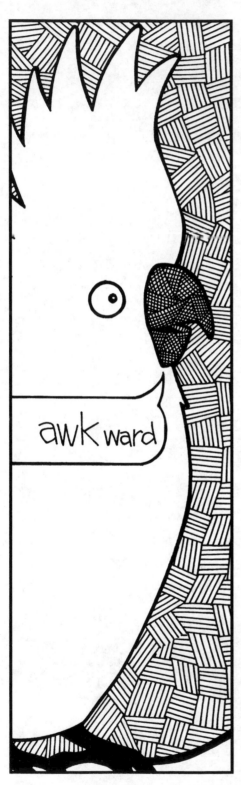
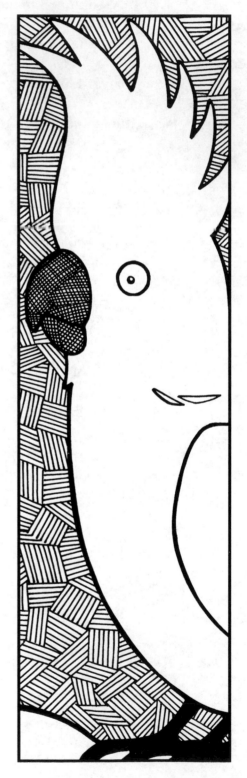

always

aisle

defense

success

different

business

desperate

terrific

doesn't

awkward

tomorrow

similar

realize

misspell

separate

* Bonus Words *

disease

possess

subtle

Frequently Misspelled Words #2

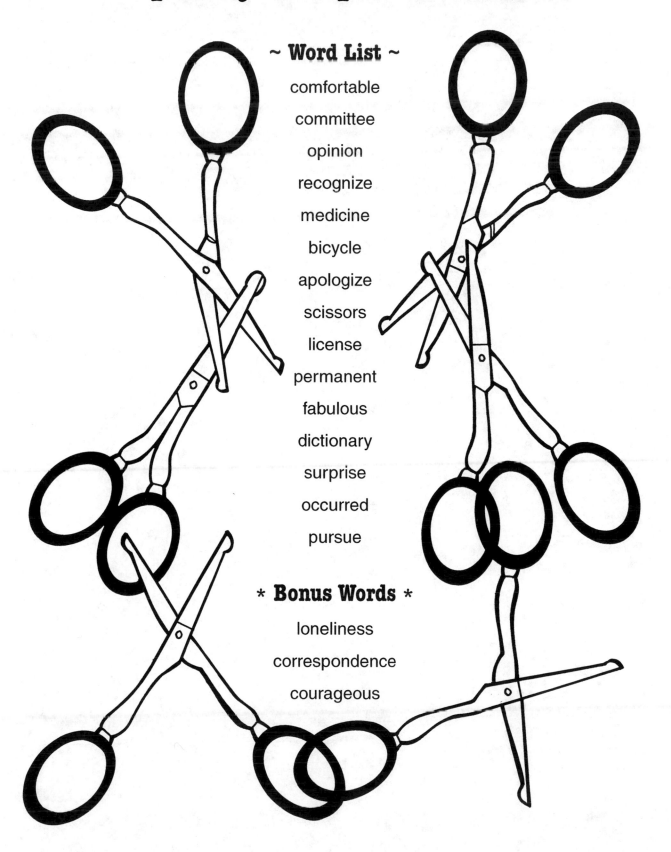

~ **Word List** ~

comfortable

committee

opinion

recognize

medicine

bicycle

apologize

scissors

license

permanent

fabulous

dictionary

surprise

occurred

pursue

* **Bonus Words** *

loneliness

correspondence

courageous

Frequently Misspelled Words #3

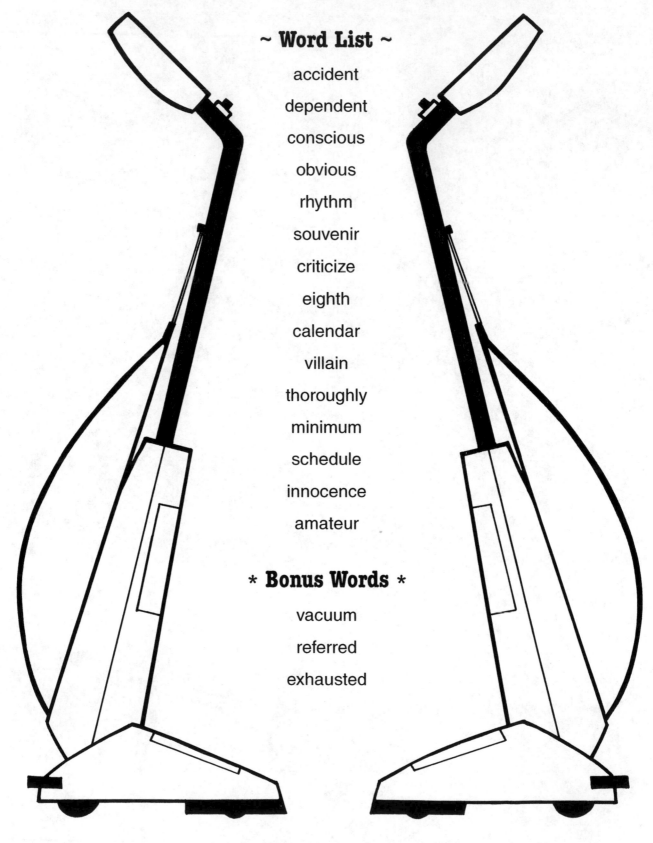

~ Word List ~

accident

dependent

conscious

obvious

rhythm

souvenir

criticize

eighth

calendar

villain

thoroughly

minimum

schedule

innocence

amateur

* Bonus Words *

vacuum

referred

exhausted

Frequently Misspelled Words #4

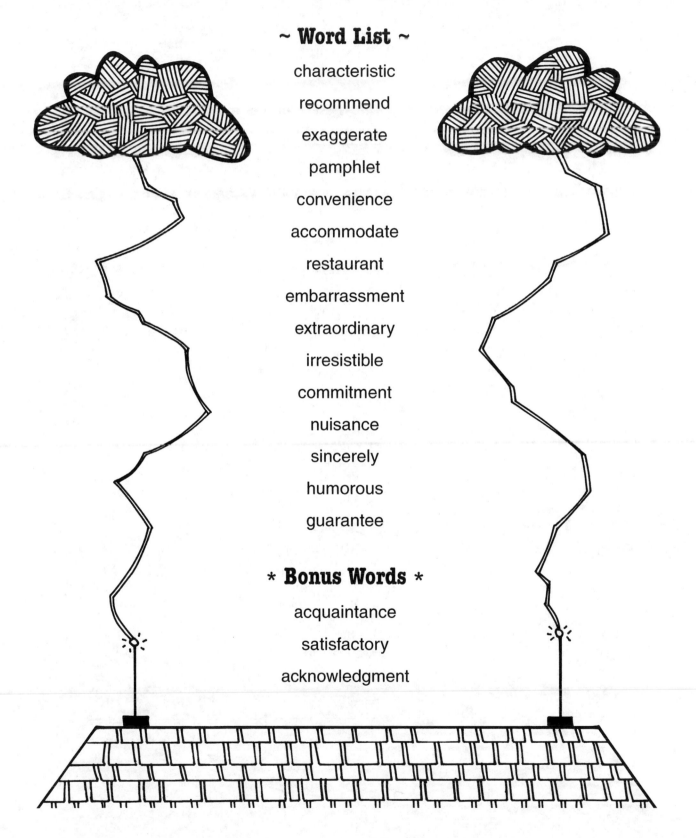

~ Word List ~

characteristic

recommend

exaggerate

pamphlet

convenience

accommodate

restaurant

embarrassment

extraordinary

irresistible

commitment

nuisance

sincerely

humorous

guarantee

* Bonus Words *

acquaintance

satisfactory

acknowledgment

Words That Are Often Confused

to	*preposition*	indicates direction or connection
too	*adverb*	also; more than enough
two	*adjective*	the number representing one plus one
its	*pronoun*	possessive form of the word *it*
it's	*pronoun; verb*	contraction for the words *it is*
whose	*pronoun*	possessive form of the word *who*
who's	*pronoun; verb*	contraction for the words *who is*
lay	*verb*	to place
lie	*verb*	to recline
there	*adverb*	at that place
their	*pronoun*	possesive form of the word *they*
they're	*pronoun; verb*	contraction for the words *they are*
all ways	*adverb*	in every possible way
always	*adverb*	at all times; forever
your	*pronoun*	possessive form of the pronoun *you*
you're	*pronoun; verb*	contraction for the words *you are*
than	*conjunction*	used in comparing things
then	*adverb*	at that time; afterwards
desert	*noun*	dry, barren land
desert	*verb*	to leave or abandon
dessert	*noun*	last course of a meal
accept	*verb*	to receive
except	*verb*	to leave out
already	*adverb*	previously
all ready	*adverb; adjective*	prepared

Words That Are Often Confused (continued)

Fill in the correct spelling word(s) in each sentence.

1. **two, too, to**

   We're going _____ open a window, because it's _____ hot in here
   by _____ in the afternoon.

2. **there, their, they're**

   _____ coming over for pizza after _____ soccer game.

3. **than, then**

   If Stephen is older _____ Michael, _____ he can go first.

4. **your, you're**

   When _____ upset, it's hard to keep _____
   cool and think clearly.

5. **all ready, already**

   Our car is _____ packed for vacation,
   and we are _____ to leave in the morning.

6. **accept, except**

   Everyone is coming with us _____ Molly; she had to
   _____ a dinner invitation.

7. **desert, dessert**

   After a month in the blazing _____, the miners were ready to
   _____ their camp and head to town for a good meal and some
   cold ice cream for _____.

More Words That Are Often Confused

loose	*adjective*	not tight-fitting
lose	*verb*	to fail to win, obtain, or gain
coarse	*adjective*	rough or crude
course	*noun*	path
personal	*adjective*	private
personnel	*noun*	a group of people employed in an office, factory, or organization
capital	*noun*	a city that is the seat of government
capitol	*noun*	the building in which a legislative body deliberates
principal	*adjective*	most important
principal	*noun*	a head man or woman
principle	*noun*	a rule or code of conduct
stationary	*adjective*	immovable
stationery	*noun*	letter paper
complement	*noun*	a completing part
compliment	*noun*	an expression of admiration
emigrate	*verb*	to leave one's own country for another
immigrate	*verb*	to come into a country of which one is not a native for permanent residence

More Words That Are Often Confused (continued)

Fill in the correct spelling word(s) in each sentence.

1. **loose, lose**

   This watch band is so _____ that I'm afraid it's going to slip off

   my wrist and I am going to _____ it.

2. **capital, capitol**

   While we were visiting Sacramento, the _____ of

   California, we went inside the _____ building.

3. **stationary, stationery**

   I need to buy more _____.

4. **complement, compliment**

   Dad paid me a nice _____ when he said my new

   scarf was a great _____ to the outfit I was wearing.

5. **principle, principal**

   The _____ of our school was just promoted.

6. **personal, personnel**

   The _____ manager of the company had to leave

   early to take care of a _____ family matter.

7. **coarse, course**

   The muddy spots on the _____ that the runners took

   had been covered with _____ sand.

Spelling Review

In each group of words, find the one word that is spelled correctly,
and fill in the bubble in front of that word. Then write that spelling word on the line.

1. ○ a. accomodate
   ○ b. embarassment
   ○ c. pamphlet
   ○ d. apolagize

   _____

2. ○ a. recommend
   ○ b. lisense
   ○ c. dictionery
   ○ d. ocurred

   _____

3. ○ a. surprize
   ○ b. different
   ○ c. awkwurd
   ○ d. mispell

   _____

4. ○ a. similiar
   ○ b. separate
   ○ c. tomorow
   ○ d. desparate

   _____

5. ○ a. sucess
   ○ b. businiss
   ○ c. terrific
   ○ d. realise

   _____

6. ○ a. comfortible
   ○ b. committe
   ○ c. scisors
   ○ d. permanent

   _____

7. ○ a. restaurant
   ○ b. irrestable
   ○ c. sincerly
   ○ d. extraordinery

   _____

8. ○ a. conveneince
   ○ b. minamum
   ○ c. fabulus
   ○ d. medicine

   _____

9. ○ a. upinion
   ○ b. bicycle
   ○ c. persue
   ○ d. deosn't

   _____

10. ○ a. defence
    ○ b. allways
    ○ c. aisle
    ○ d. recognise

   _____

~ Content Area ~
Spelling Words

Bird Words

~ Word List ~

ostrich

eagle

penguin

condor

egret

oriole

quail

parakeet

chicken

cardinal

flamingo

pelican

pigeon

swallow

woodpecker

* Bonus Words *

cuckoo

meadowlark

pheasant

General Science Words #1

~ Word List ~

meteor

dinosaur

magnet

mammal

physics

vaccine

zoology

mineral

volcano

molecule

pollution

planet

fossil

disease

nucleus

* Bonus Words *

electricity

oceanography

invertebrate

General Science Words #2

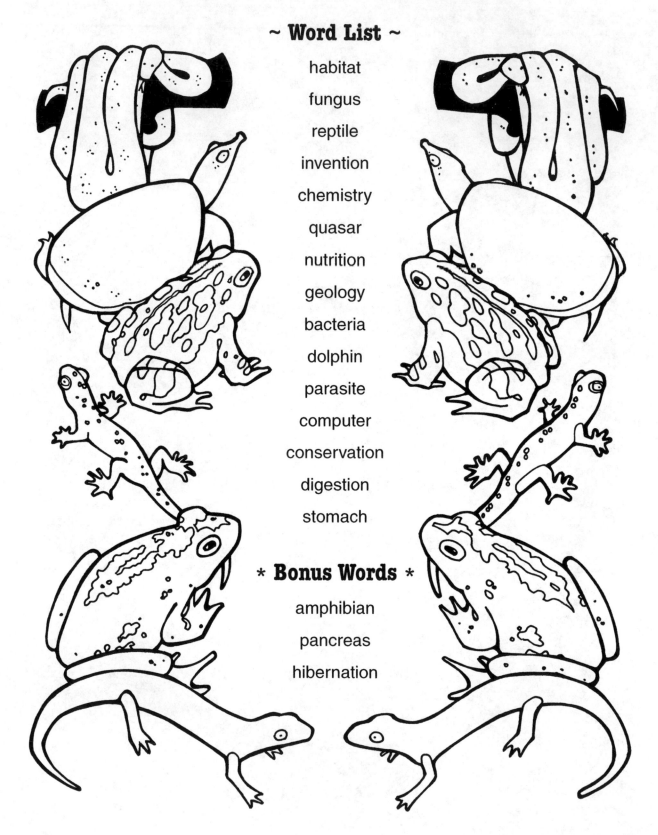

~ Word List ~

habitat

fungus

reptile

invention

chemistry

quasar

nutrition

geology

bacteria

dolphin

parasite

computer

conservation

digestion

stomach

* Bonus Words *

amphibian

pancreas

hibernation

Machine Words

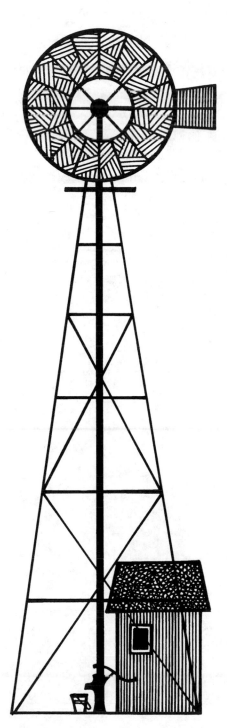

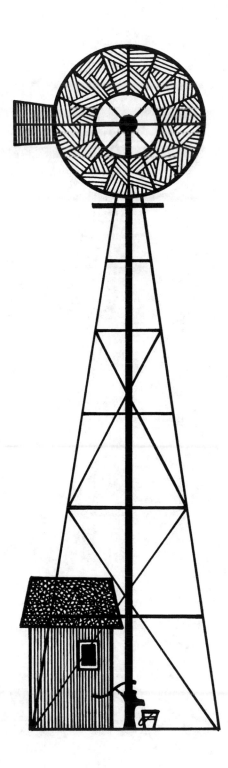

~ Word List ~

catapult

pulley

windmill

turbine

derrick

machine

treadmill

waterwheel

axle

screw

generator

wedge

crane

inclined plane

lever

* Bonus Words *

caliper

carburetor

microscope

* Just for Fun

Pick the names of two machines from this list. Do research to learn more about them.
Draw and label diagrams to show how these two machines work.

Mammal Words

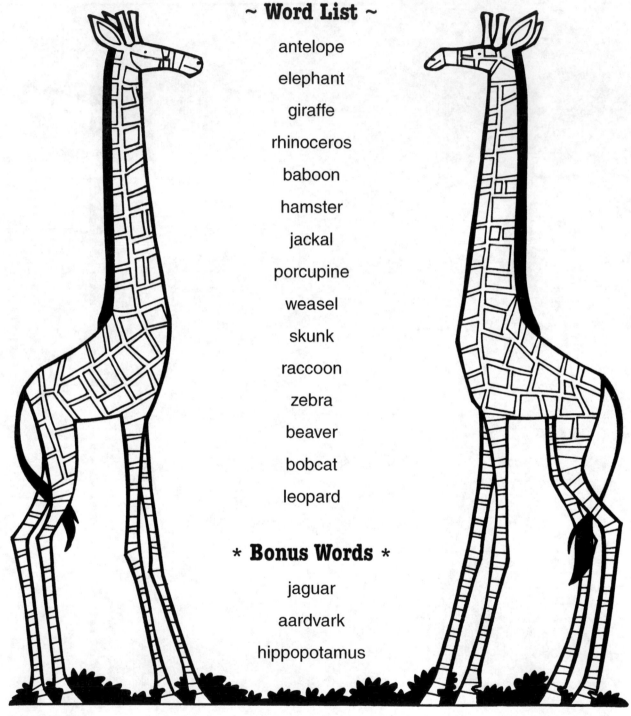

~ Word List ~

antelope

elephant

giraffe

rhinoceros

baboon

hamster

jackal

porcupine

weasel

skunk

raccoon

zebra

beaver

bobcat

leopard

* Bonus Words *

jaguar

aardvark

hippopotamus

* Just for Fun

Write a short story using one of the animals from your spelling list as the main character.

Plant Words

~ Word List ~

blossom

thorn

dormant

algae

perennial

transpiration

pollination

annual

embryo

graft

osmosis

deciduous

petal

pistil

sepal

* **Bonus Words** *

xylem

chlorophyll

photosynthesis

Rain Forest Words

~ Word List ~

canopy

gibbon

centipede

ecosystem

iguana

macaw

orchid

equator

anaconda

python

rainfall

sloth

lemur

toucan

* Bonus Words *

camouflage

philodendron

tarantula

* Just for Fun

Get together with your classmates, and draw a rain forest mural illustrating as many of these spelling words as possible. Feel free to add pictures of other rain forest plants and animals.

Skeleton Words

~ Word List ~

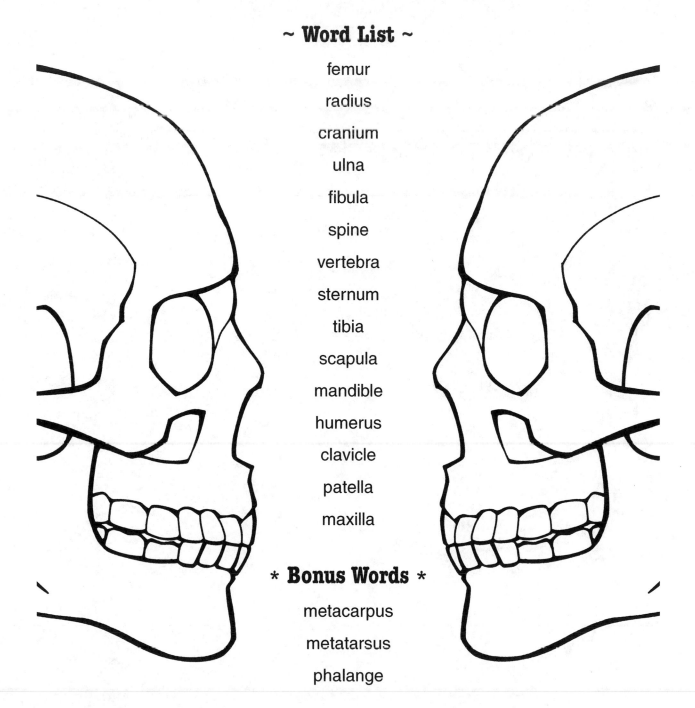

femur

radius

cranium

ulna

fibula

spine

vertebra

sternum

tibia

scapula

mandible

humerus

clavicle

patella

maxilla

* Bonus Words *

metacarpus

metatarsus

phalange

* Just for Fun

Do research to find where each of these bones is located in the human body.

Skeleton Words (continued)

Using your spelling words on page 81, unscramble the names of these bones.
Write the correct spelling on the lines below.

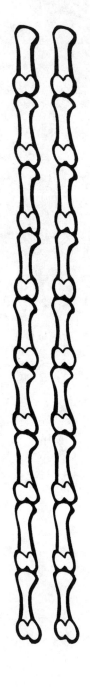

1. nlua _____

2. bitia _____

3. refum _____

4. pisen _____

5. bufial _____

6. surdia _____

7. taplale _____

8. cusalap _____

9. mushuer _____

10. xalmila _____

11. enturms _____

12. leviclac _____

Space Words

~ Word List ~

altitude

orbit

planet

corona

eclipse

asteroid

astronomy

galaxy

telescope

meteorite

comet

supernova

gravity

nebula

constellation

* Bonus Words *

chromosphere

apogee

equinox

* Just for Fun

Write a science fiction story that takes place in outer space. Use five or more of these spelling words in your story.

Weather Words

~ Word List ~

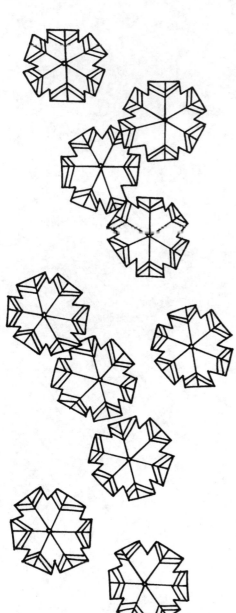

blizzard

moisture

temperature

cirrus

tornado

cyclone

hurricane

atmosphere

icicle

barometer

lightning

drizzle

hailstone

thunder

humidity

* Bonus Words *

precipitation

typhoon

cumulostratus

* Just for Fun

Imagine that you are the weather forecaster on a television station covering weather across the country. Write a weather report for your viewing audience that uses as many words from your list as possible.

Super Challenge Bonus Words #1
Aches and Pains

Words that end in *-itis* usually name an inflammation in the human body.
Take the challenge and learn to spell these super hard words!

~ Word List ~

hepatitis

encephalitis

gingivitis

cystitis

laryngitis

neuritis

colitis

arthritis

nephritis

dermatitis

conjunctivitis

gastritis

bronchitis

tonsillitis

appendicitis

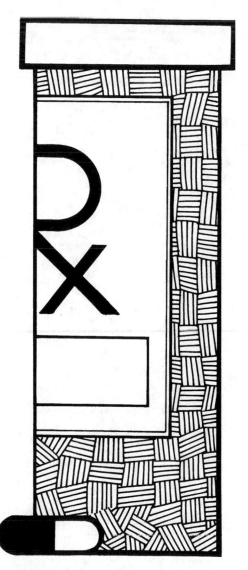

✶ Just for Fun

Do research to learn what part of the body is inflamed for each of these words. Create a matching game for a classmate to solve with the *-itis*es listed on the right-hand side of your paper and the body parts on the left-hand side. Be sure to change the order in which the body parts are listed so that the *-itis*es are not in the same order as the correct answers.

85

Super Challenge Bonus Words #2
Phobias

A *phobia* is an intense or unreasonable fear of some particular thing.

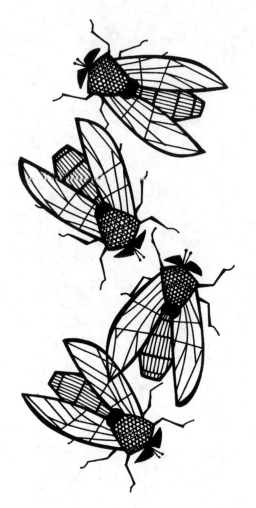

~ Word List ~

acrophobia

hemophobia

agoraphobia

claustrophobia

phonophobia

pyrophobia

thalassophobia

hydrophobia

demophobia

thanatophobia

hypnophobia

ailurophobia

entomophobia

autophobia

cynophobia

Just for Fun

* On a separate piece of paper, write each of your *phobia* spelling words, and then match these definitions by writing each one by the correct phobia word.

- fear of people or crowds
- fear of death
- fear of heights
- fear of sleep
- fear of cats
- fear of flames or fire
- fear of open spaces
- fear of insects
- fear of being alone
- fear of small spaces
- fear of dogs
- fear of water
- fear of noise
- fear of the ocean or sea
- fear of blood

Super Challenge Bonus Words #3
Fields of Study

~ Word List ~

geologist

podiatrist

cardiologist

astronomer

ornithologist

geophysicist

philatelist

criminologist

botanist

graphologist

entomologist

herpetologist

ophthalmologist

archaeologist

dermatologist

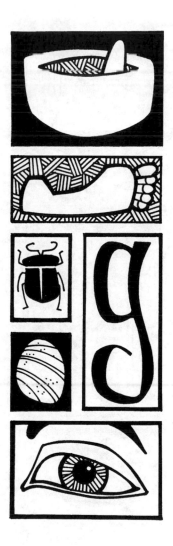

★ Just for Fun

Write the spelling words listed above on a separate piece of paper. Next to each word, write the word(s) below that best describes that field of study.

- reptiles and amphibians
- celestial bodies
- crime
- plants
- earth

- insects
- birds
- rocks
- feet
- eyes

- skin
- handwriting
- heart
- stamps
- ancient civilizations

Super Challenge Bonus Words #4
Math Words

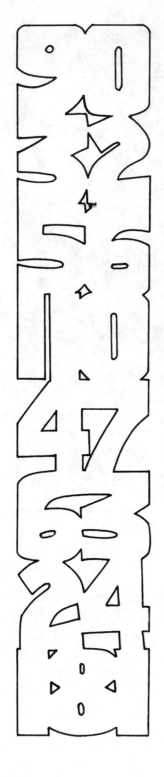

~ Word List ~

decimal

multiplication

addition

diameter

exponent

acute

geometry

integer

ratio

parallel

percentile

quotient

remainder

radius

probability

* Bonus Words *

circumference

perpendicular

equivalent

Communication Words

~ Word List ~

braille

telephone

poster

gesture

newspaper

postcard

telegram

magazine

cable

brochure

radio

telegraph

banner

satellite

television

* Bonus Words *

pictograph

semaphore

hieroglyphics

* Just for Fun

Write an invitation for a friend to join you at an amusement park by using one of the forms of communication listed above. Be creative! Write the invitation in braille, design a postcard, or create a brochure.

Early American Colonial Words

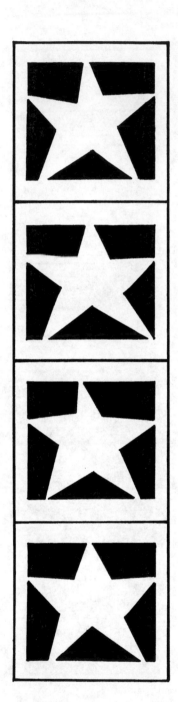

~ Word List ~

breeches

plantation

blacksmith

colonist

flax

gristmill

hornbook

indigo

pillory

musket

mansion

pewter

venison

hatchet

candle

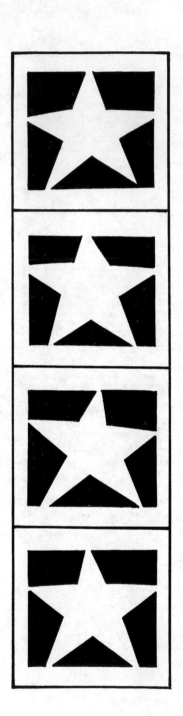

* Bonus Words *

plague

sconce

doublet

* Just for Fun

Draw pictures of six of your spelling words and label them.

Family Words

~ Word List ~

mother

father

sister

brother

grandmother

grandfather

cousin

parents

aunt

uncle

relative

mother-in-law

father-in-law

stepmother

stepfather

* Bonus Words *

ancestor

genealogy

nephew

General Social Studies Words

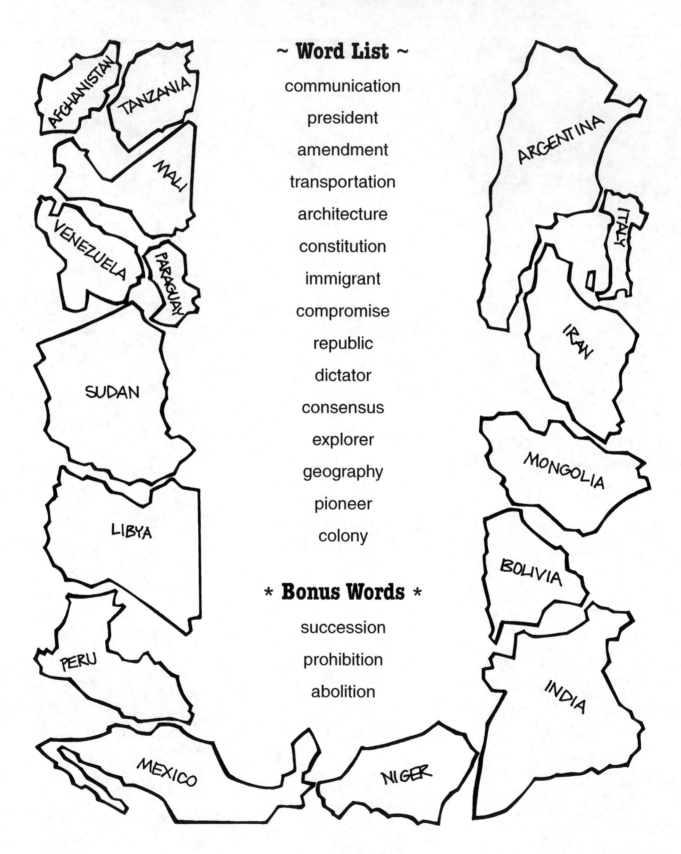

~ Word List ~

communication

president

amendment

transportation

architecture

constitution

immigrant

compromise

republic

dictator

consensus

explorer

geography

pioneer

colony

* Bonus Words *

succession

prohibition

abolition

Geography Words

~ Word List ~

canyon

plateau

wetlands

lagoon

peninsula

delta

mountain

tributary

reservoir

waterfall

glacier

forest

island

bayou

erosion

* Bonus Words *

veldt

isthmus

fjord

* Just for Fun

Draw and color a landscape which includes many of the geographical features named in this list. Label your drawing, adding other words as needed.

Occupation Words

~ Word List ~

teacher

actress

surgeon

dentist

sculptor

attorney

composer

inventor

florist

gardener

carpenter

librarian

consultant

investigator

engineer

* Bonus Words *

chauffeur

psychologist

veterinarian

* Just for Fun

Play charades with your class by forming teams and taking turns selecting one of the words from this list to communicate without speaking or writing.

Sports Words

~ Word List ~

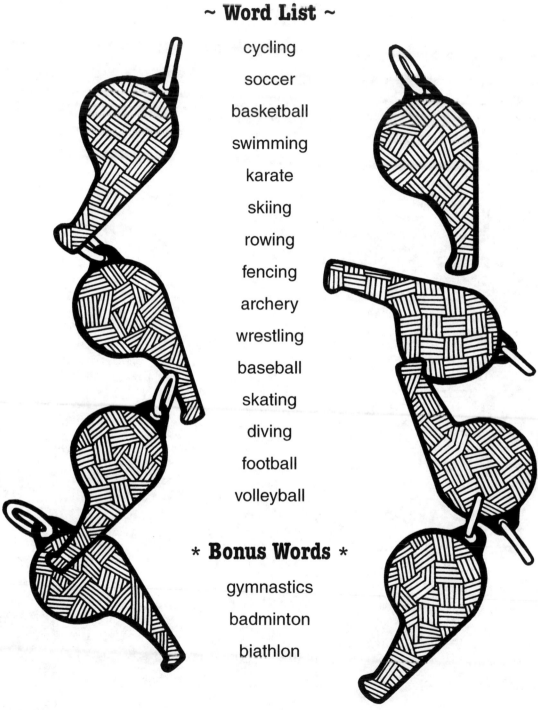

cycling

soccer

basketball

swimming

karate

skiing

rowing

fencing

archery

wrestling

baseball

skating

diving

football

volleyball

* Bonus Words *

gymnastics

badminton

biathlon

* Just for Fun

Write a short story with one of these sports as its theme. Be sure you have an exciting beginning to grab your readers.

Transportation Words

~ Word List ~

ambulance

submarine

bicycle

escalator

motorcycle

monorail

scooter

helicopter

airplane

skateboard

tricycle

tractor

canoe

trolley

automobile

✶ Bonus Words ✶

yacht

dinghy

hydrofoil

✶ Just for Fun

Make a transportation book in which you illustrate and define each means of transportation listed above.

~ Fun with ~
Spelling Words

Fun with Spelling Words

✱ Rebus Puzzles

A *rebus* is a puzzle made up of syllables or words that appear in the form of pictures.

> examples: mail + man = mailman
> in + vest + i + gate = investigate

Pick six or more words from your spelling list. Create a rebus for each word. Your pictures can represent parts of your word (such as letters or syllables), or the entire word.

✱ Parts of Speech

Write the part of speech for each word on your spelling list. If a word can be used as more than one part of speech, list all the choices. Then write ten sentences which each use a different word from your list. Underline the spelling word in each sentence and tell what part of speech it is.

✱ Graph Those Syllables

Divide your spelling words into syllables. Use your dictionary if you need help. Make a graph to show the results.

✱ Secret Codes

Create a code by designing a symbol for each letter of the alphabet. Write your spelling words in this code. Then give your code and word list to a classmate to solve.

Fun with Spelling Words

★ Silly Sentences

Pick ten words from your spelling list. Use each one in a sentence containing several words beginning with the same sound as the spelling word. Underline the spelling word in each sentence. Illustrate your two favorite sentences on a separate piece of paper.

example: spelling word: *field*

Freddy and four funny friends flew frisbees in the <u>field</u> on Friday.

★ Tic-Tac-Toe Code

A Tic-Tac-Toe code is based on the positions of letters within a tic-tac-toe grid and within the spaces formed by an **X**. Each letter is represented by the lines that define the space the letter occupies.

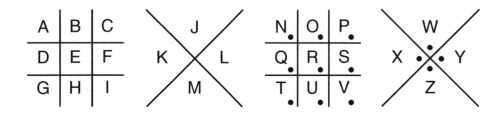

example: happy =

Pick ten words from your spelling list. On a separate piece of paper, write the words in tic-tac-toe code instead of letters. Exchange codes with a classmate, and write the correct spelling for each coded word.

Fun with Spelling Words

★ Memory Spelling Challenge

Write each of your spelling words on two index cards, one word per card. Shuffle all the cards, and place them face down in even rows on a large table or on the floor. Challenge a classmate to see who can find the most matching pairs of spelling words by taking turns turning over two cards at a time. If a player finds two cards with the same spelling word, he or she keeps the pair and takes another turn. If two cards are picked that do *not* match, the player places them face down where he or she found them. The next player then takes a turn. Play continues in this manner until all of the cards have been taken. The player with the most pairs is the winner.

Secret Vowel Code

★ Write your spelling words on a sheet of notebook paper. Using the following code, substitute a number for each vowel as shown below. Give your spelling list along with the code to a classmate. Ask him or her to write the correct spelling of each word on the list as shown.

CODE
A = 9
E = 7
I = 5
O = 3
U = 2

example:

spelling word: *miserable*

= M5S7R9BL7

Fun with Spelling Words

✳ Make a Thesaurus

A *thesaurus* is a book that lists words and their synonyms. Write your spelling words in alphabetical order on notebook paper. Then write one or more synonyms for each word. Use your dictionary or an actual thesaurus for help.

✳ E-Mail Message

Write an e-mail message to a friend on your computer. Use ten or more of your spelling words. Underline each spelling word in your message.

✳ Cheerful Spelling

Write a cheer for two or more of your words to help you learn the correct spelling. Teach your cheers to a group of friends in your class. Present your cheers to your entire class as a fun way to review for your next spelling test.

example: spelling word: *delightful*

Give me a D and an E, that's DE
Then add a L-I-G-H-T!
End with an F-U-L
What do you have?
DELIGHTFUL!
Say it again—DELIGHTFUL!
Yea!

Fun with Spelling Words

★ Crossword Puzzle

Make a crossword puzzle using words from your spelling list. Write and number word clues as shown. Your spelling words should be written going vertically and horizontally.

ACROSS

1. Bird of Antarctica
3. Red-headed bird
5. Tall pink bird
6. Parrot-like pet

DOWN

1. Carrier _____
2. State bird of Maryland
4. White wading bird

★ Make a Word

Select a long word from your spelling list. See how many words of three or more letters you can make using only the letters in your chosen word. Proper nouns are not allowed. Plurals are allowed only if the letter *s* appears in your spelling word. You may only use letters the number of times they appear in your spelling word.

> example: spelling word = entertain
> *teen* is allowed because there are two *e*'s in the word *entertain*
> but the word *attain* is not allowed because there is only one *a* in the word *entertain*.

Repeat this exercise for four other words from your spelling list.

★ Mixed-Up Spelling

Pick ten words from your spelling list, and mix up the letters in each one. Write the scrambled words on a piece of paper numbering them from one through ten. Exchange papers with a classmate, and unscramble the words, spelling them correctly.

Fun with Spelling Words

★ Spelling Poems

Pick a spelling word from your list. Write a poem about yourself starting each line with a letter from the word you selected. Your poem does not have to rhyme.

example: spelling word: *interest*

I love playing Scrabble,
Never cared much for asparagus or Brussel sprouts,
Talk on the phone with my friends,
Enjoy playing golf and being outdoors,
Red is my favorite color,
Enjoy reading and I always
Spend lots of time browsing in bookstores,
Take my dog Jake for a walk every morning before school.

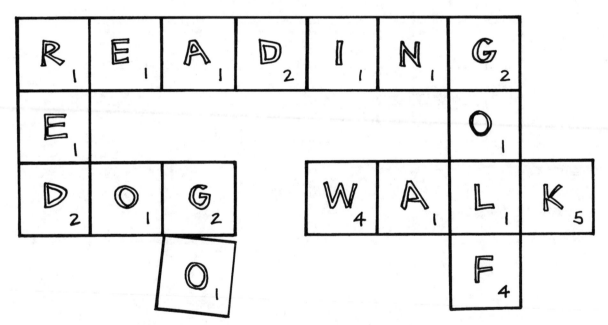

★ Word Search Puzzle

Make up a word search puzzle for a friend to solve using all the words from your spelling list. Use the grid on page 104. Fill in any empty boxes with letters. Write the spelling words below the grid so your friend will know the words to look for. Ask him or her to circle each spelling word found in the puzzle.

Fun with Spelling Words

Word Search Puzzle

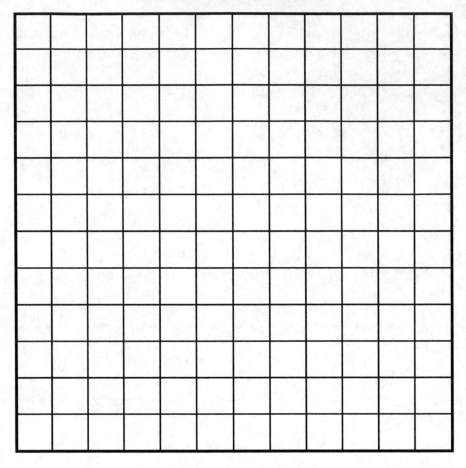

Spelling Words

_____   _____

_____   _____

_____   _____

_____   _____

_____   _____

_____   _____

_____   _____

_____   _____

Fun with Spelling Words

★ Spelling Scavenger Hunt #1

Can you find and write words from your spelling list that fit each of these descriptions?

- a compound word _____ _____

- a word that begins with a prefix _____

- a word that ends with a suffix _____

- a word that has more than one meaning _____

(write the various meanings of the word)_____

_____

_____

- a word with exactly five letters _____

- a word with exactly six letters _____

- a word with vowels at both ends _____

- a word with consonants at both ends _____

Fun with Spelling Words

✱ Spelling Scavenger Hunt #2

Can you find and write words from your spelling list that fit each of these descriptions?

- a word that starts and ends with the same letter _____

- a word containing a pair of like consonants, such as *letter* _____

- a word with two vowels together _____

- a word "ing" can be added to _____

- a word with exactly seven letters_____

- a word with exactly eight letters _____

- a word that can be made plural _____

- a word that "ly" can be added to _____

Spelling Progress Chart

Student's name: _____

Page →	15	17	19	22	24	27	30	33	35	37
Number of correct answers ↓										
10										
9										
8										
7										
6										
5										
4										
3										
2										
1										
0										

107

Spelling Progress Chart

Student's name: _____

Page ➔	39	41	43	45	47	48	51	53	57	58	
Number of correct answers ↓											
10											20
											19
9											18
											17
8											16
											15
7											14
											13
6											12
											11
5											10
											9
4											8
											7
3											6
											5
2											4
											3
1											2
											1
0											0

~ Answer Key ~

Page 15: Words with the Prefixes *co-, col-, con-, com-,* **and** *cor-*
1. c
2. a
3. c
4. d
5. b
6. a
7. c
8. d
9. b
10. c

Page 17: Words with the Prefix *dis-*
1. b
2. d
3. b
4. a
5. c
6. d
7. c
8. d
9. b
10. d

Page 19: Words with the Prefix *mis-*
1. a
2. b
3. d
4. b
5. c
6. c
7. b
8. a
9. c
10. d

Page 20: Words with the Prefix *mis-*
1. I
2. D
3. B
4. F
5. G
6. C
7. H
8. A
9. E

words with two syllables (in any order)
misuse
misplace
mislead
mistreat
mishap
misprint
misjudge

words with three syllables
misfortune
mispronounce
misinform
mishandle
misconduct
mismanage
misbehave

word with four syllables
misunderstand

Page 22: Words with the Prefix *pre-*
1. d
2. b
3. a
4. c
5. b
6. d
7. b
8. d
9. c
10. a

Page 24: Words with the Prefix *pro-*
1. d
2. b
3. c
4. a
5. d
6. c
7. d
8. c
9. d
10. b

Page 25: Words with the Prefix *pro-*

A	P	E	N	U	O	N	O	R	P	O	C
R	P	R	O	H	I	B	I	T	R	P	L
O	Y	R	J	P	M	A	R	G	O	R	P
C	P	R	O	T	R	U	D	E	V	P	A
S	K	T	L	C	N	O	A	K	I	R	M
E	E	C	G	M	E	P	T	Y	D	O	P
R	K	E	L	Y	L	D	X	E	E	M	R
U	U	T	N	P	O	Z	U	Q	S	O	O
G	R	O	T	C	E	J	O	R	P	T	D
O	A	R	P	R	O	F	I	L	E	E	U
R	C	P	R	O	J	E	C	T	K	A	C
P	P	N	M	I	A	L	C	O	R	P	E

prolific fish

Page 27: Words with the Prefix *re-*

1. c
2. a
3. d
4. b
5. c
6. c
7. b
8. c
9. a
10. c

Page 28: Words with the Prefix *re-*

1. remain
2. retrace
3. reminder
4. redirect
5. removable
6. rebuild
7. reporter
8. recovered

1. C
2. F
3. J
4. H
5. G
6. B
7. I
8. D
9. A
10. E

Page 30: Words with the Prefix *un-*

1. c
2. b
3. c
4. d
5. b
6. c
7. a
8. c
9. d
10. a

Page 33: Words with the Suffixes *-able* **and** *-ible*

1. d
2. a
3. c
4. b
5. d
6. d
7. b
8. d
9. a
10. c

Page 35: Words with the Suffixes *-ance* **and** *-ence*

1. a
2. d
3. c
4. b
5. d
6. a
7. c
8. d
9. c
10. b

Page 37: Words with the Suffixes *-ar, -er, -or,* **and** *-r*

1. a
2. c
3. b
4. d
5. c
6. c
7. d
8. a
9. c
10. d

Page 39: Words with the Suffix *-ful*

1. c
2. d
3. a
4. c
5. b
6. d
7. a
8. d
9. c
10. d

Page 41: Words with the Suffix *-ly*

1. c
2. b
3. c
4. a
5. c
6. b
7. a
8. c
9. d
10. c

Page 43: Words with the Suffix *-ment*

1. c
2. d
3. c
4. b
5. a
6. d
7. b
8. c
9. b
10. c

Page 45: Words with the Suffix -sion

1. a
2. d
3. d
4. b
5. c
6. a
7. d
8. c
9. d
10. b

Page 47: Words with the Suffixes -tion and -ion

1. c
2. b
3. a
4. c
5. d
6. a
7. c
8. b
9. d
10. c

Page 48: Prefix and Suffix Review

1. b
2. a
3. c
4. c
5. a
6. c
7. c
8. d
9. b
10. d

Page 51: Words with i-e and e-i #1

1. b. niece
2. b. chief
3. a. ceiling
4. a. neither
5. b. believe
6. b. yield
7. b. grief
8. b. field
9. b. siege
10. a. their
11. b. thief
12. b. pier
13. b. piece
14. b. brief
15. a. weight

Page 53: Words with i-e and e-i Review

1. b. yield
2. d. receive
3. a. foreign
4. c. perceive
5. c. efficient
6. b. ancient

1. weight
2. field
3. friend
4. pier
5. mischief
6. reign
7. siege
8. believe

Page 57: Spelling Plurals of Nouns

1. b
2. b
3. a
4. a
5. a
6. a
7. b
8. a
9. b
10. a
11. b
12. a
13. b
14. a
15. a
16. a
17. a
18. b
19. a
20. b

Page 58: Spelling Plurals of Nouns

1. b
2. a
3. a
4. b
5. b
6. b
7. a
8. b
9. b
10. b
11. b
12. a
13. a
14. a
15. b
16. b
17. a
18. b
19. b
20. b

Page 61: Homophone Review: Word List #1

1. allowed, aloud
2. yolk, flour
3. capital
4. hoarse
5. thrown, horse
6. need, grate
7. plane, hangar
8. beach
9. great, waist
10. strait
11. hanger
12. capitol

111

Page 63: Homophone Review: Word List #2

1. currant
2. cymbal
3. fowl
4. stationery
5. thyme
6. principal
7. shear
8. coarse
9. colonel
10. counsel

Page 69: Words That Are Often Confused

1. to, too, two
2. They're, their
3. than, then
4. you're, your
5. already, all ready
6. except, accept
7. desert, desert, dessert

Page 71: More Words That Are Often Confused

1. loose, lose
2. capital, capitol
3. stationery
4. compliment, complement
5. principal
6. personnel, personal
7. course, coarse

Page 72: Spelling Review

1. c
2. a
3. b
4. b
5. c
6. d
7. a
8. d
9. b
10. c

Page 82: Skeleton Words

1. ulna
2. tibia
3. femur
4. spine
5. fibula
6. radius
7. patella
8. scapula
9. humerus
10. maxilla
11. sternum
12. clavicle

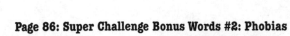

Page 86: Super Challenge Bonus Words #2: Phobias

acrophobia	fear of heights
hemophobia	fear of blood
agoraphobia	fear of open spaces
claustrophobia	fear of narrow or closed places
phonophobia	fear of sounds or noise
pyrophobia	fear of fire or flames
thalassophobia	fear of ocean or sea
hydrophobia	fear of water
demophobia	fear of people or crowds
thanatophobia	fear of death
hypnophobia	fear of sleep
ailurophobia	fear of cats
entomophobia	fear of insects
autophobia	fear of being alone with oneself
cynophobia	fear of dogs

Page 87: Super Challenge Bonus Words #3: Fields of Study

geologist	rocks
podiatrist	feet
cardiologist	heart
astronomer	celestial bodies
ornithologist	birds
geophysicist	the earth
philatelist	stamps
criminologist	crime
botanist	plants
graphologist	handwriting
entomologist	insects
herpetologist	reptiles and amphibians
ophthalmologist	eyes
archaeologist	ancient civilizations
dermatologist	skin

Page 102: Crossword Puzzle

Across: 1. Penguin; 3. Woodpecker; 5. Flamingo; 6. Parakeet
Down: 1. Pigeon; 2. Oriole; 4. Egret